TO BE A **BLACK WOMAN:**

Portraits in Fact and Fiction

Edited by MEL WATKINS *and* JAY DAVID

New York 1970
WILLIAM MORROW AND COMPANY, INC.

We are most grateful to Catherine Greene for her
creative assistance in the preparation of this book.

Acknowledgments

Grateful acknowledgment is made to:

Delacorte Press, for permission to reprint material from *Silent Voices* by Josephine Carson. Copyright © 1969 by Josephine Carson and used by permission of the publisher.

The Macmillan Company, for permission to reprint material from *Manchild in the Promised Land* by Claude Brown. Copyright © 1965 by Claude Brown.

Harper & Row, Publishers, Inc., for permission to reprint material from *A Street in Bronzeville* by Gwendolyn Brooks. Copyright 1945 by Gwendolyn Brooks Blakely.

Harper & Row, Publishers, Inc., for permission to reprint material from *Uncle Tom's Children* by Richard Wright. Copyright 1937 by Richard Wright.

Lethonia Gee Heard, for permission to reprint "By Glistening, Dancing Seas."

Indiana University Press, for permission to reprint material from "Mulatto: A Tragedy of the Deep South" from *Five Plays by Langston Hughes*. Copyright © 1963 by Langston Hughes.

University of Chicago Press, for permission to reprint material from *Lay My Burden Down: A Folk History of Slavery*, edited by B. A. Botkin.

University of Chicago Press, for permission to reprint material from *The Negro Family in the United States* by E. Franklin Frazier.

McGraw-Hill Book Company, for permission to reprint material from *Soul on Ice* by Eldridge Cleaver. Copyright © 1968 by Eldridge Cleaver.

Liveright, Publishers, New York, for permission to reprint "Blood-burning Moon" from *Cane* by Jean Toomer. Copyright © 1951 by Jean Toomer.

Doubleday and Company, Inc., for permission to reprint material from *Lady Sings the Blues* by Billie Holiday with William Dufty. Copyright © 1956 by Eleanora Fagan and William F. Dufty.

Doubleday and Company, Inc., for permission to reprint material from *Sex and Racism in America* by Calvin C. Hernton. Copyright © by Calvin C. Hernton.

Alfred A. Knopf, Inc., for permission to reprint "Mother to Son" from *Selected Poems* by Langston Hughes. Copyright 1926 by Alfred A. Knopf, Inc., and renewed 1954 by Langston Hughes.

The Dial Press, for permission to reprint material from *Another Country* by James Baldwin. Copyright © 1960, 1962 by James Baldwin.

Broadside Press, for permission to reprint material from *Don't Cry, Scream* by Don L. Lee. Copyright © 1969 by Don L. Lee.

Grove Press, Inc., for permission to reprint material from *The Autobiography of Malcolm X*. Copyright © 1964 by Alex Haley and Malcolm X. Copyright © 1965 by Alex Haley and Betty Shabazz.

William Morris Agency, Inc., for permission to reprint *Health Card* by Frank Yerby. Copyright © 1944 by Frank Yerby.

Basic Books, Inc., Publishers, New York, for permission to reprint Chapter III of *Black Rage* by William H. Grier, M.D., and Price M. Cobbs, M.D. Copyright © 1968 by William H. Grier and Price M. Cobbs.

The Sterling Lord Agency, for permission to reprint material from *In White America* by Martin Duberman, published by New American Library. Copyright © 1965 by Martin Duberman.

Farrar, Straus & Giroux, Inc., for permission to reprint material from *The Flagellants* by Carlene Hatcher Polite.

Random House, Inc., for permission to reprint "For de Lawd" from *Good Times* by Lucille Clifton. Copyright © 1969 by Lucille Clifton.

Random House, Inc., for permission to reprint material from *I Know Why the Caged Bird Sings* by Maya Angelou. Copyright © 1969 by Maya Angelou.

The Lucy Kroll Agency, for permission to reprint material from *The Mark of Oppression* by Abram Kardiner, M.D., and Lionel Ovesey, M.D., published by The World Publishing Company. Copyright © 1951 by Abram Kardiner and Lionel Ovesey.

Mrs. W. E. B. Du Bois, for permission to reprint material from *Darkwater* by W. E. B. Du Bois.

Lena Horne, and *Show* Magazine, for permission to reprint "I Just Want to Be Myself" by Lena Horne.

Atlantic-Little, Brown and Company, for permission to reprint material from *Children of Crisis* by Robert Coles, M.D. Copyright © 1964, 1965, 1966, 1967 by Robert Coles.

Paule Marshall, for permission to reprint "Reena."

Random House, Inc., for permission to reprint material from *A Raisin in the Sun* by Lorraine Hansberry. Copyright © 1958, 1959, 1966 by Robert Nemiroff as Executor of the Estate of Lorraine Hansberry.

Rolls Royce Music Co., for permission to reprint "Four Women" by Nina Simone. Copyright © 1966 by Rolls Royce Music Co., c/o Copyright Service Bureau, 221 West 57th Street. All rights reserved.

The Macmillan Company, for permission to reprint material from *Black Bourgeoisie* by E. Franklin Frazier. Copyright © by The Free Press, a Corporation, 1957.

Mari E. Evans, for permission to reprint her poem "When In Rome," from *American Negro Poets,* by Arna Bontemps.

Bob Bennett, for permission to reprint his poem " (Title)," from *Black Fire,* edited by LeRoi Jones and Larry Neal. Copyright © 1968 by LeRoi Jones and Larry Neal.

Contents

FOUR WOMEN

Nina Simone

My skin is black,
   My arms are long.
My hair is wooly,
   My back is strong;
Strong enough to take the pain
   Inflicted again and again.
What do they call me?
   My name is Aunt Sarah—
   My name is Aunt Sarah.

My skin is yellow,
   My hair is long.
Between two worlds
   I do belong.
My father was rich and white,
   He forced my mother late
   one night.

What do they call me?
  My name is Safronia—
  My name is Safronia.

My skin is tan,
  My hair is fine.
My lips invite you,
  My mouth like wine.
Whose little girl am I?
  Anyone who has money to buy.
What do they call me?
  My name is Sweet Thing—
  My name is Sweet Thing.

My skin is brown,
  My manner is tough.
I'll kill the first mother I see,
  My life has been rough.
I'm awfully bitter these days,
  Because my parents were slaves.
What do they call me?
  My name is PEACHES!

Introduction

THE American black woman has occupied a unique if unenviable position in the United States. Historically she has borne the weight of inferior status and prejudice derived from her sex as well as her color. In part, this may explain the conspicuous absence of a substantial body of literature written by or about black women; the black female writer has been more rare than her white counterpart, and black men, overwhelmed with the problem of their own emasculation, have usually avoided the subject. Consequently, the black woman has been treated only tangentially in American literature and in most previous sociological studies, and no indepth portrait has been available in a single volume.

This book attempts to provide such a portrait. Each of the selections presented reflects upon or explicates some salient or characteristic aspect of the black woman's experience in America. They span American history from the antebellum period, when black women were brought to America expressly for the purpose of breeding more slaves, to today's complex technological society. The excerpts included are varied in form as well as content: They range from sociological studies and essays to the intense, personal depictions offered by autobiographies, poetry, and fiction; they reflect the hardships and bitterness of the black woman's experience as well as the joy and gratification that she has achieved despite the intensity of her oppression. As a whole, these selections provide a testimony that substantiates the claim of sociologist Calvin Hernton that the black woman, "more than anyone else, has borne the constant agonies of racial barbarity in America" and, also, attest to the strength of spirit that has helped her to survive that barbarity.

The arrangement of these excerpts also suggests something of the dynamics of the different roles the black woman has played in American life. As the words of Nina Simone's song "Four Women" suggest, these roles have been varied and contradictory. She has endured physical labor and toil—as slave, and later, as breadwinner—that is virtually unknown by the vast majority of white women. Forcibly transplanted to our shores, she was made the vessel into which white puritanical America poured its repressed sexuality. She became the sexual myth incarnate—a plaything, an illicit pleasure for the white man. To some extent, she accepted the myth and often adopted a life style that actualized it. Yet she remained a protector and provider for her family—a cushion for her men and children against the hostility and violence of the outside world. Finally, in the past decade, she has become deeply involved in the black man's fight for equal rights; she has begun the agonizing process of re-evaluating and redefining herself in black terms. In the multiplicity of these images and the subtle processes by which they have emerged and overlapped lies the true portrait of the black woman in America.

All save six of these authors (Martin Duberman; Robert Coles, M.D.; Abram Kardiner, M.D. and Lionel Ovesey, M.D.; Josephine Carson; and B. A. Botkin) are black; through all these selections perhaps some of the illusions and misconceptions concerning black women will be dispelled. If so, the readers of this volume will have gained some understanding of the legacy of being a black female in America. Moreover, they may begin to understand the intensity of the cry of "freedom now" and the unremitting militancy with which that demand is being made.

MEL WATKINS AND JAY DAVID

New York City

THE BURDEN
OF OPPRESSION

THE most indelible experiences of black women in America grew out of the treatment they received as slaves. Hard labor, poor food and little shelter, the inhumane breeding of more slaves, the rigors of keeping her master's house and children, and the passive acceptance of any white man's advances—all were part of the black woman's life.

Emancipation brought few meaningful improvements to the lives of black women and their families. Black men were still unable to protect their women from sexual assaults by white men without the threat of mob reprisal. The absolute power of white men versus the powerlessness of blacks often made compliance a necessity for her. There was little relief from the burden of physical labor. Employment for black men was sporadic and difficult to find, and the inadequate wages they were paid could rarely support a family. Their women were thus forced to seek jobs, in many instances becoming the sole providers for their families. Thus, although their status was changed from "slave" to "freedman," their environment and the conditions of their lives were still dominated by the exploitation that had characterized slavery.

Physical oppression, however, was not the heaviest burden that black women bore. Their roles as wives and mothers were grotesquely distorted by the pressures of a hostile outside world. Even as a wife, the black woman was not beyond the sexual exploitation of white men; and as a mother she was forced to accept her adolescent daughters' plight in the same white hands that had abused her. The black mother found it necessary to instill in her children a distrust and fear of the white world, and she often discouraged their ambitions in order that they might more easily accept the second-class citizenship awaiting them.

These experiences presaged much of the black woman's personality today and molded the matrilineal character of the black family. The following selections reflect the black female's debasement and humiliation at the hands of white America, and they cast into relief the profound psychological scars that became part of her heritage.

1

"Jenny Proctor" (Interviewed during the late 1930's)

FROM

Lay My Burden Down: A Folk History of Slavery

Edited by B. A. Botkin

Although a few still contend that slavery benevolently pro-
vided for a primitive people unfit to provide for themselves,
most now acknowledge the atrocities that were an essential
part of that institution. Still, it is rare that the plight of the
black woman is discussed in relation to slavery in America.

In the following autobiographical account, a former slave,
Jenny Proctor, describes her experience as property in Ala-
bama—an experience that was typical—during the mid-nine-
teenth century. The narrative shows too how slavery often
eroded blacks' assessment of themselves. After Emancipation,
Jenny Proctor, like many freed slaves, worked with her hus-
band as a sharecropper, first on her former master's land, and
then on a farm in Texas.

I'S HEAR tell of them good slave days, but I ain't never seen
no good times then. My mother's name was Lisa, and when I
was a very small child I hear that driver going from cabin to
cabin as early as 3 o'clock in the morning, and when he comes
to our cabin he say, "Lisa, Lisa, git up from there and git that
breakfast." My mother, she was cook, and I don't recollect
nothing 'bout my father. If I had any brothers and sisters I

didn't know it. We had old ragged huts made out of poles and some of the cracks chinked up with mud and moss and some of them wasn't. We didn't have no good beds, just scaffolds nailed up to the wall out of poles and the old ragged bedding throwed on them. That sure was hard sleeping, but even that feel good to our weary bones after them long hard days' work in the field. I 'tended to the children when I was a little gal and tried to clean the house just like Old Miss tells me to. Then soon as I was ten years old, Old Master, he say, "Git this here nigger to that cotton patch."

I recollects once when I was trying to clean the house like Old Miss tell me, I finds a biscuit, and I's so hungry I et it, 'cause we never see such a thing as a biscuit only sometimes on Sunday morning. We just have corn bread and syrup and sometimes fat bacon, but when I et that biscuit and she comes in and say, "Where that biscuit?" I say, "Miss, I et it 'cause I's so hungry." Then she grab that broom and start to beating me over the head with it and calling me low-down nigger, and I guess I just clean lost my head 'cause I knowed better than to fight her if I knowed anything 't all, but I start to fight her, and the driver, he comes in and he grabs me and starts beating me with that cat-o'-nine-tails, and he beats me till I fall to the floor nearly dead. He cut my back all to pieces, then they rubs salt in the cuts for more punishment. Lord, Lord, honey! Them was awful days. When Old Master come to the house, he says, "What you beat that nigger like that for?" And the driver tells him why, and he say, "She can't work now for a week. She pay for several biscuits in that time." He sure was mad, and he tell Old Miss she start the whole mess. I still got them scars on my old back right now, just like my grandmother have when she die, and I's a-carrying mine right on to the grave just like she did.

Our master, he wouldn't 'low us to go fishing—he say that too easy on a nigger and wouldn't 'low us to hunt none either—but sometime we slips off at night and catch possums. And when Old Master smells them possums cooking 'way in the night, he wraps up in a white sheet and gits in the chimney corner and scratch on the wall, and when the man in the cabin goes to the door and say, "Who's that?" he say, "It's me, what's ye cooking in there?" and the man say, "I's cooking possum." He say "Cook him and bring me the hindquarters and you and the wife and the children eat the rest." We never had no chance to git any rabbits 'cept when we was a-clearing and grubbing the new ground. Then we catch some rabbits, and if they looks good to the white folks they takes them and if they no good the niggers git them. We never had no gardens. Sometimes the slaves git vegetables from the white folks' garden and sometimes they didn't.

Money? Uh-uh! We never seen no money. Guess we'd-a bought something to eat with it if we ever seen any. Fact is, we wouldn't-a knowed hardly how to bought anything, 'cause we didn't know nothing 'bout going to town.

They spinned the cloth what our clothes was made of, and we had straight dresses or slips made of lowell.[1] Sometimes they dye 'em with sumac berries or sweet-gum bark, and sometimes they didn't. On Sunday they make all the children change, and what we wears till we gits our clothes washed was gunny sacks with holes cut for our head and arms. We didn't have no shoes 'cepting some homemade moccasins, and we didn't have them till we was big children. The little children they goes naked till they was big enough to work. They was soon big enough though, 'cording to our master. We had red flannel for winter underclothes. Old Miss she say a sick nigger cost more than the flannel.

Weddings? Uh-uh! We just steps over the broom and we's married. Ha! Ha! Ha!

Old Master he had a good house. The logs was all hewed off smooth-like, and the cracks all fixed with nice chinking, plumb 'spectable-looking even to the plank floors. That was something. He didn't have no big plantation, but he keeps

1. A cheap cotton cloth made in Lowell, Mass.

'bout three hundred slaves in them little huts with dirt floors. I thinks he calls it four farms what he had.

Sometimes he would sell some of the slaves off of that big auction block to the highest bidder when he could git enough for one.

When he go to sell a slave, he feed that one good for a few days, then when he goes to put 'em up on the auction block he takes a meat skin and greases all round that nigger's mouth and makes 'em look like they been eating plenty meat and such like and was good and strong and able to work. Sometimes he sell the babes from the breast, and then again he sell the mothers from the babes and the husbands and the wives, and so on. He wouldn't let 'em holler much when the folks be sold away. He say, "I have you whupped if you don't hush." They sure loved their six children though. They wouldn't want nobody buying them.

We might-a done very well if the old driver hadn't been so mean, but the least little thing we do he beat us for it and put big chains round our ankles and make us work with them on till the blood be cut out all around our ankles. Some of the masters have what they call stockades and puts their heads and feet and arms through holes in a big board out in the hot sun, but our old driver he had a bull pen. That's only thing like a jail he had. When a slave do anything he didn't like, he takes 'em in that bull pen and chains 'em down, face up to the sun, and leaves 'em there till they nearly dies.

None of us was 'lowed to see a book or try to learn. They say we git smarter than they was if we learn anything, but we slips around and gits hold of that Webster's old blue-back speller and we hides it till 'way in the night and then we lights a little pine torch,[2] and studies that spelling book. We learn it too. I can read some now and write a little too.

They wasn't no church for the slaves, but we goes to the white folks' arbor on Sunday evening, and a white man he gits

2. Several long splinters of rich pine, of a lasting quality and making a bright light.

up there to preach to the niggers. He say, "Now I takes my text, which is, Nigger obey your master and your mistress, 'cause what you git from them here in this world am all you ever going to git, 'cause you just like the hogs and the other animals—when you dies you ain't no more, after you been throwed in that hole." I guess we believed that for a while 'cause we didn't have no way finding out different. We didn't see no Bibles.

Sometimes a slave would run away and just live wild in the woods, but most times they catch 'em and beats 'em, then chains 'em down in the sun till they nearly die. The only way any slaves on our farm ever goes anywhere was when the boss sends him to carry some news to another plantation or when we slips off way in the night. Sometimes after all the work was done a bunch would have it made up to slip out down to the creek and dance. We sure have fun when we do that, most times on Saturday night.

All the Christmas we had was Old Master would kill a hog and give us a piece of pork. We thought that was something, and the way Christmas lasted was 'cording to the big sweet-gum backlog what the slaves would cut and put in the fireplace. When that burned out, the Christmas was over. So you know we all keeps a-looking the whole year round for the biggest sweet gum we could find. When we just couldn't find the sweet gum, we git oak, but it wouldn't last long enough, 'bout three days on average, when we didn't have to work. Old Master he sure pile on them pine knots, gitting that Christmas over so we could git back to work. . . .

We didn't have much looking after when we git sick. We had to take the worst stuff in the world for medicine, just so it was cheap. That old blue mass and bitter apple would keep us out all night. Sometimes he have the doctor when he thinks we going to die, 'cause he say he ain't got anyone to lose, then that calomel what that doctor would give us would pretty nigh kill us. Then they keeps all kinds of lead bullets and asafetida balls round our necks, and some carried a rabbit foot with them all the time to keep off evil of any kind.

Lord, Lord, honey! It seems impossible that any of us ever lived to see that day of freedom, but thank God we did.

2

"The Slave Auction"

by Frances E. W. Harper
(First published 1854)

FROM

Poems on Various Subjects

*One of the most degrading experiences for the black woman
was her sale on the auction block, where she was stripped and
publicly paraded before the eyes of potential buyers. The following poem vividly recreates the scene of a slave auction and
expresses some of the agony the black woman was forced to
endure.*

*Frances Ellen Watkins Harper, the author, although her-
self free, witnessed the treatment of black women under slavery and expressed her abhorrence in her writing as well as in
other facets of her life. She is said to have been the most popular American Negro poet of her time, and during her lifetime (1825–1911) published four volumes of poetry. She was
also active in the Underground Railroad and several reform
movements, including the Abolitionists.*

THE SLAVE AUCTION

The sale began—young girls were there,
    Defenceless in their wretchedness,
Whose stifled sobs of deep despair
    Revealed their anguish and distress.

And mothers stood with streaming eyes,
   And saw their dearest children sold;
Unheeded rose their bitter cries,
   While tyrants bartered them for gold.

And woman, with her love and truth—
   For these in sable forms may dwell—
Gaz'd on the husband of her youth,
   With anguish none may paint or tell.

And men, whose sole crime was their hue,
   The impress of their Maker's hand,
And frail and shrinking children, too,
   Were gathered in that mournful band.

Ye who have laid your love to rest,
   And wept above their lifeless clay,
Know not the anguish of that breast,
   Whose lov'd are rudely torn away.

Ye may not know how desolate
   Are bosoms rudely forced to part,
And how a dull and heavy weight
   Will press the life-drops from the heart.

3

FROM

Mulatto: A Tragedy of the Deep South

by Langston Hughes
(First produced 1935)

Since liaisons between black female slaves and white men were common during slavery, the large number of mulatto children that were produced is not surprising. Treatment of these children varied with individual slaveholders: some freed their offspring, while others simply shunted them off to the fields or perhaps allowed them to work in the big house as servants. Nevertheless, the offspring of slave mothers and white masters, whether freedmen or slaves, often represented a dissident faction in the highly structured antebellum environment; being a part of both the black and the white world, they were more likely to resist accepting the slave's abysmal plight. Even after Emancipation, the position of such children of mixed parentage remained anomalous.

For their mothers, they represented an obvious dilemma. In the following selection, set in the nineteen-twenties, one black mother, Cora, has seen her son Bert flee after murdering Col. Thomas Norwood, his father. A white man has discovered the body and called the sheriff when Cora begins her monologue. In this play, Langston Hughes (1902–1967) reveals the pathos of the black mother's confused and divided loyalty to her mulatto child and his white father.

CORA: My boy can't get to de swamp now. They's telephoned the white folks down that way. So he'll come back home now. Maybe he'll turn into de crick and follow de branch home directly. *(Protectively)* But they shan't get him. I'll make a place for to hide him. I'll make a place upstairs down under de floor, under ma bed. In a minute ma boy'll be runnin' from de white folks with their hounds and their ropes and their guns and everything they uses to kill po' colored folks with. *(Distressed)* My boy'll be out there runnin'. *(Turning to the body on the floor)* Colonel Tom, you hear me? Our boy, out there runnin'. *(Fiercely) You* said he was ma boy—*ma* bastard boy. I heard you . . . but he's yours too . . . but yonder in de dark runnin'—runnin' from yo' people, from white people. *(Pleadingly)* Why don't you get up and stop 'em? He's *your* boy. His eyes is gray—like your eyes. He's tall like you's tall. He's proud like you's proud. And he's runnin'—runnin' from po' white trash what ain't worth de little finger o' nobody what's got your blood in 'em, Tom. *(Demandingly)* Why don't you get up from there and stop 'em, Colonel Tom? What's that you say? He ain't your chile? He's ma bastard chile? My yellow bastard chile? *(Proudly)* Yes, he's mine. But don't call him that. Don't you touch him. Don't you put your white hands on him. You's beat him enough, and cussed him enough. Don't you touch him now. He *is* ma boy, and no white folks gonna touch him now. That's finished. I'm gonna make a place for him upstairs under ma bed. *(Backs away from the body toward the stairs)* He's ma chile. Don't you come in ma bedroom while he's up there. Don't you come to my bed no mo'. I calls you to help me now, and you just lays there. I calls you for to wake up, and you just lays there. Whenever you called me, in de night, I woke up. When you called for me to love, I always reached out ma arms fo' you. I borned you five chilluns and now one of 'em is out yonder in de dark runnin' from yo' people. Our youngest boy out yonder in de dark runnin'. *(Accusingly)* He's runnin' from you, too. You said he warn't your'n—he's just Cora's po' little yellow bastard. But he *is* your'n,

Colonel Tom. *(Sadly)* And he's runnin' from you. You are out yonder in de dark, *(Points toward the door)* runnin' our chile, with de hounds and de gun in yo' hand, and Talbot's followin' 'hind you with a rope to hang Robert with. *(Confidently)* I been sleepin' with you too long, Colonel Tom, not to know that this ain't you layin' down there with yo' eyes shut on de floor. You can't fool me—you ain't never been so still like this before—you's out yonder runnin' ma boy. *(Scornfully)* Colonel Thomas Norwood, runnin' ma boy through de fields in de dark, runnin' ma poor little helpless Bert through de fields in de dark to lynch him . . . Damn you, Colonel Norwood! *(Backing slowly up the stairs, staring at the rigid body below her)* Damn you, Thomas Norwood! God damn you!

[Later; the body has been removed.]

CORA *comes downstairs, looks for a long moment out into the darkness, then closes the front door and draws the blinds. She looks down at the spot where the* COLONEL's *body lay:* All de colored folks are runnin' from you tonight. Po' Colonel Tom, you too old now to be out with de mob. You got no business goin', but you had to go, I reckon. I 'members that time they hung Luke Jordon, you sent yo' dogs out to hunt him. The next day you killed all de dogs. You were kinder softhearted. Said you didn't like that kind of sport. Told me in bed one night you could hear them dogs howlin' in yo' sleep. But de time they burnt de courthouse when that po' little cullud boy was locked up in it cause they said he hugged a white girl, you was with 'em again. Said you had to go help 'em. Now you's out chasin' ma boy. *(As she stands at the window, she sees a passing figure)* There goes yo' other woman, Colonel Tom, Livonia is runnin' from you too, now. She would've wanted you last night. Been wantin' you again ever since she got old and fat and you stopped layin' with her and put her in the

kitchen to cook. Don't think I don't know, Colonel Tom.
Don't think I don't remember them nights when you used
to sleep in that cabin down by de spring. I knew 'Vonia was
there with you. I ain't no fool, Colonel Tom. But she ain't
bore you no chilluns. I'm de one that bore 'em. *(Musing)*
White mens, and colored womens, and little bastard chilluns—that's de old way of de South—but it's ending now.
Three of your yellow brothers yo' father had by Aunt Sallie Deal—what had to come and do your laundry to make
her livin'—you got colored relatives scattered all over this
county. Them de ways o' de South—mixtries, mixtries.

CORA: *(Bending over the spot on the floor where the* COLO-
NEL *has lain. She calls)* Colonel Tom! Colonel Tom! Colonel Tom! Look! Bertha and Sallie and William and Bert,
all your chilluns, runnin' from you, and you layin' on de
floor there, dead! *(Pointing)* Out yonder with the mob,
dead. And when you come home, upstairs in my bed on top
of my body, dead. *(Goes to the window, returns, sits down,
and begins to speak as if remembering a far-off dream)*
Colonel Thomas Norwood! I'm just poor Cora Lewis. Colonel Norwood. Little black Cora Lewis, Colonel Norwood.
I'm just fifteen years old. Thirty years ago, you put your
hands on me to feel my breasts, and you say, "You a pretty
little piece of flesh, ain't you? Black and sweet, ain't you?"
And I lift up ma face, and you pull me to you, and we laid
down under the trees that night, and I wonder if your
wife'll know when you go back up the road into the big
house. And I wonder if my mama'll know it, when I go
back to our cabin. Mama said she nursed you when you was
a baby, just like she nursed me. And I loved you in the
dark, down there under that tree by de gate, afraid of you
and proud of you, feelin' your gray eyes lookin' at me in de
dark. Then I cried and cried and told ma mother about it,
but she didn't take it hard like I thought she'd take it. She
said fine white mens like de young Colonel always took

good care o' their colored womens. She said it was better than marryin' some black field hand and workin' all your life in de cotton and cane. Better even than havin' a job like ma had, takin' care o' de white chilluns. Takin' care o' you, Colonel Tom. *(As* CORA *speaks the sounds of the approaching mob gradually grow louder and louder. Auto horns, the howling of dogs, the far-off shouts of men, full of malignant force and power, increase in volume)* And I was happy because I liked you, 'cause you was tall and proud, 'cause you said I was sweet to you and called me purty. And when yo' wife died—de Mrs. Norwood *(Scornfully)* that never bore you any chilluns, the pale beautiful Mrs. Norwood that was like a slender pine tree in de winter frost . . . I knowed you wanted me. I was full with child by you then—William, it was—our first boy. And my mammy said, go up there and keep de house for Colonel Tom, sweep de floors and make de beds, and by and by, you won't have to sweep de floors and make no beds. And what ma mammy said was right. It all come true. Sam and Rusus and 'Vonia and Lucy did de waitin' on you and me, and de washin' and de cleanin' and de cookin'. And all I did was a little sewin' now and then, and a little preservin' in de summer and a little makin' of pies and sweet cakes and things you like to eat on Christmas. And de years went by. And I was always ready for you when you come to me in de night. And we had them chilluns, your chilluns and mine, Tom Norwood, all of 'em! William, born dark like me, dumb like me, and then Baby John what died; then Bertha, white and smart like you; and then Bert with your eyes and your ways and your temper, and mighty nigh your color; then Sallie, nearly white, too, and smart, and purty. But Bert was yo' chile! He was always yo' child . . . Good-looking, and kind, and headstrong, and strange, and stubborn, and proud like you, and de one I could love most 'cause he needed de most lovin'. And he wanted to call you "papa," and I tried to teach him no, but he did it anyhow and *(Sternly)* you beat him, Colonel Thomas Norwood. And he growed up with de beatin' in his heart, and your eyes in his head, and your ways, and your pride. And this summer he looked like you that time I first knowed you down by de road under them trees, young and fiery and proud. There was no touchin' Bert, just like there was no touchin' you. I could only love him, like I loved you. I could only love him. But I couldn't talk to him, because he hated you. He had your ways—and you beat him! After you beat that chile, then you died, Colonel Norwood. You died here in this house, and you been living dead a long time. You lived dead. *(Her voice rises above the nearing sounds of the mob)* And when I said this evenin', "Get up! Why don't you help me?" you'd done been dead a long time—a long time before you laid down on this floor here, with the breath choked out o' you—and Bert standin' over you living, living, living. That's why you hated him. And you want to kill him. Always, you wanted to kill him. Out there with de hounds and de torches and de cars and de guns, you want to kill my boy. But you won't kill him! He's comin' home first. He's comin' home to me. He's comin' home!

4

"The Ethics of Living Jim Crow"

by Richard Wright
(First published 1940)

FROM

Uncle Tom's Children

The debasement of black women did not cease with the end of the Civil War and chattel slavery. Between 1865 and 1877 the terrorists in the South were somewhat restrained by the Reconstruction governments, although black people in both the North and South were never completely shielded from racist violence. After Reconstruction, however, the temporary restraints were removed. The barbarous treatment of blacks that characterized slavery was reinstated with "Jim Crow" laws.

The following selection, from the autobiographical essays of Richard Wright (1908–1960), illustrates the plight of the black woman living under the "separate but equal" ethic of the Jim Crow South. This incident occurred in Mississippi during Wright's childhood, but the situation it depicts was not uncommon in other sections of the United States in the early twentieth century.

MY Jim Crow education continued on my next job, which was portering in a clothing store. One morning, while polishing brass out front, the boss and his twenty-year-old son got out of their car and half dragged and half kicked a Negro woman into the store. A policeman standing at the corner looked on, twirling his night-stick. I watched out of the corner of my eye, never slackening the strokes of my chamois upon the brass. After a few minutes, I heard shrill screams coming from the rear of the store. Later the woman stumbled out, bleeding, crying, and holding her stomach. When she reached the end of the block, the policeman grabbed her and accused her of being drunk. Silently, I watched him throw her into a patrol wagon.

When I went to the rear of the store, the boss and his son were washing their hands in the sink. They were chuckling. The floor was bloody and strewn with wisps of hair and clothing. No doubt I must have appeared pretty shocked, for the boss slapped me reassuringly on the back.

"Boy, that's what we do to niggers when they don't want to pay their bills," he said, laughing.

His son looked at me and grinned.

"Here, hava cigarette," he said.

Not knowing what to do, I took it. He lit his and held the match for me. This was a gesture of kindness, indicating that even if they had beaten the poor old woman, they would not beat me if I knew enough to keep my mouth shut.

"Yes, sir," I said, and asked no questions.

After they had gone, I sat on the edge of a packing box and stared at the bloody floor till the cigarette went out.

That day at noon, while eating in a hamburger joint, I told my fellow Negro porters what had happened. No one seemed surprised. One fellow, after swallowing a huge bite, turned to me and asked:

"Huh! Is tha' all they did t' her?"

"Yeah. Wasn't tha' enough?" I asked.

"Shucks! Man. She's a lucky bitch!" he said, burying his lips deep into a juicy hamburger. "Hell, it's a wonder they didn't lay her when they got through."

5

"The Negro Woman"

by Calvin C. Hernton
(First published 1965)

FROM

Sex and Racism in America

*In reaction to the abuse of the white world, the black woman
has often had to become stronger, less "feminine" than her
white sister; the luxury of feminine innocence and demure-
ness has largely been denied her. She has also been forced to
devise ways (usually not condoned by middle-class ethics) of
surviving in a hostile white world.*

*Calvin Hernton, author and sociologist, in the following
selection describes the violent and historically circumscribed
world of the black woman and reveals some of her survival
methods.*

I AM quite aware of the fact that from time to time in America various individuals and groups besides Negroes have been
victims of prejudice, discrimination, injustice, persecution,
and outright murder. I am referring to American Indians,
Poles, Jews, Mexicans, Puerto Ricans, labor groups, anarchists,
and so on. But it has been the Negro woman, more than anyone else, who has borne the constant agonies of racial barbarity in America, from the very first day she was brought in
chains to this soil. The Negro woman through the years has
suffered (and endured) every sexual outrage (with all of the
psychological ramifications) that a "democratic" society can

possibly inflict upon a human being. The sexual atrocities that the Negro woman has suffered in the United States, South and North, and what these atrocities have done to her personality as a female creature, is a tale more bloody and brutal than most of us can imagine. I believe it was a black woman who first uttered the words: "Nobody knows the trouble I've seen."

As slaves Negro women were brought to the New World, specifically North America, for only one reason—to serve as breeding animals for more slaves. Simultaneously they served as body toys for their white masters. True, Negro women performed many other tasks during slavery. They worked in the fields, cooked, ironed, served as servants and nurses. But these roles were secondary. Their white master, as Lillian Smith writes:

. . . mated with these dark women whom they had dehumanized in their minds, and fathered by them children who, according to their race philosophy, were "without souls"—a strange exotic new kind of creature whom they made slaves of and . . . sold on the auction block.[1]

It is important to understand the "race philosophy" of the ante-bellum South and how this philosophy affected the sexuality of the Negro woman. Black people were not considered to be human beings. They were wild, savage creatures "without souls." Negro women were *forced* to give up their bodies like animals to white men at random! Cash writes:

. . . the Negro woman . . . *torn* from her tribal *restraints* and *taught* an easy complaisance for commercial reasons, was to be had for the taking. Boys on and about the plantation inevitably learned to use her, and having acquired the habit, often continued it into manhood and even after marriage. . . .[2]

1. Lillian Smith, *Killers of the Dream* (Garden City, New York: Doubleday Anchor Books, 1961), p. 103.
2. W. J. Cash, *The Mind of the South* (New York: Vintage Books, 1960), p. 87. My italics.

Being *torn* from the sexual restraints of her native culture (Africa) and universally *forced* to behave like a "naked savage," the relatively restrained African woman was transformed sexually into a beast. Ultimately, after experiencing the ceaseless sexual immorality of the white South, the Negro woman became "promiscuous and loose," and could be "had for the taking." Indeed, she came to look upon herself as the South viewed and treated her, for she had no other morality by which to shape her womanhood, she had no womanhood so far as the white South was concerned. And, make no mistake, it was the whole of the South who so used her and not merely "southern white trash."

Repeatedly, people who visited the ante-bellum South were shocked to find such striking resemblances between the white master of the house and some of his black slaves. Those Negro women (and there were many) who tried to maintain a measure of dignity in regard to their sex were beaten, burned, lynched, and treated worse than dogs. For example, no law was violated when, in 1838, a North Carolina slaveowner admitted that he burnt the left side of a Negro woman's face with a hot iron, which caused her to run away with her two boys, one of whom was as light as the slaveowner. The same slaveowner admitted branding the letter "R" on the cheek of a sixteen-year-old Negro girl; he also cropped a piece of her ear, and branded the same letter on the *inside* of both of her legs! [3]

When any group of women has to submit to such atrocities, when they are denied the smallest privacy of body, when they have to stand in public before men and women naked on an auction block and be fingered in the most intimate places, it is absurd to ask them to esteem themselves as restrained ladies and conduct their sexual activities along the lines of female refinement. The fiber of the human personality is not that independent of the milieu in which it has to struggle for

3. See Maude White Katz, "The Negro Woman and the Law," *Freedomways*, Vol. II, No. 3, p. 282.

sanity. It was in this way, then, that the Negro woman during slavery began to develop a depreciatory concept of herself not only as a female but as a human being as well. She did not have much of an alternative.

Then came the Civil War, followed by several turbulent but most courageous years in American history—Reconstruction. Great efforts were made to lift the Negro out of his state of degradation. In modern parlance, there was an all-out drive to change the "image" of colored people. Noxious laws were removed from the statute books; there were strong sanctions against polygamy and promiscuity; and for the first time marriages of Negro women were universally legalized. Negro men began to demand that all women of color be treated with respect and courtesy, to insist that white men stop seducing and raping black women. In 1874 a Negro congressman proclaimed the following: "We want more protection from the whites invading our homes and destroying the virtue of our women than they from us." [4]

But, alas, it was all in vain. No sooner were these measures underway, than Reconstruction ended. With the election of Hayes as President in 1876, the North compromised with the South, Union troops were withdrawn, and the Negro woman found herself again in the merciless hands of an embittered and barbarous South. The Ku Klux Klan, the Knights of the White Camellia, and other such hate groups spread like wildfire throughout the South. Rapes of Negro women were as common as "whistling Dixie."

From 1891 to 1921 the South lynched forty-five Negro women, several of whom were young girls from fourteen to sixteen years old. (This was the number of lynchings acknowledged!). . . . One victim was in her eighth month of pregnancy. Members of the mob suspended her from a tree by her ankles. Gasoline was poured on her clothes and ignited. A chivalrous white man took his knife and split open her abdomen. The unborn child fell to the ground. A member of the mob crushed its head with his heel. . . . Another

4. Ibid., p. 283.

victim was burned at the stake with her husband before a crowd of one thousand persons. . . .[5]

No, these things did not happen in Nazi Germany, thirteenth-century Europe, or during the time that Voltaire wrote *Candide*. They took place in the South, in the United States of America, in the nineteenth and twentieth centuries! Add to this the fact that, after the failure and betrayal of Reconstruction by the North, thousands of Negro men were left helpless and hopeless, uneducated and without any means of securing a livelihood. Their property was taken, and their citizenship was denied. The South succeeded in taking out its grief and bitterness against the Negro in every way possible.

Consequently the black woman in the South was left without any protection whatever. Even if a Negro male were around when a white man seduced, insulted, or raped his woman, what could he do, unarmed and outnumbered as he was? So once more the black woman was beaten back into slavery. Once more she became a sex toy and a domestic peon. She scrubbed floors, washed and ironed dirty clothes, cooked and served the white South's food. She suckled and reared the white South's children, and she was "had" almost for the taking by any white man who desired her. She must have been a strong creature with the resignation of a saint, for, while she did these things for the white South, she also maintained her own shack and supported and fought with her "shiftless" black man. She brought up her own children—the sons to be, if not lynched, "castrated" in one way or another by the ethic of living Jim Crow; the daughters to be the body toys of white men. And, somehow, she survived—she sang the gospel all day Sunday and moaned the blues throughout the week. From Bessie Smith, Mammy Yancey and Mamie Smith, right on down to Billie Holiday and Mahalia Jackson, there is no one in the world who can bring tears to your eyes like a black woman singing the blues.

5. Ibid., p. 284.

It is against this historical, socioeconomic, and moral backdrop that the sexual behavior of the Negro woman must be analyzed. When one considers the fact that (until recently) the major area of employment open to Negro women has been in the field of domestic service, it is easy to understand why and how so many black women have engaged in sexual relations with white men. Such relations may be viewed as a sort of "occupational hazard." Even today, throughout the entire South, white men are able to extort sexual pleasures from Negro women in the course of the women's employment, or in the course of their seeking employment.

The same trend may be observed in the North. There are numerous "employment agencies" that specialize in "recruiting" Negro girls from the South by glamorous advertising (i.e., the agencies offer to pay the train fare, promise high salaries in rich white Northern homes, etc.). There are several such agencies in Manhattan and the surrounding suburbs. Many of the young girls who respond to these alluring offers are soon disillusioned and end up in one of the northern ghettos such as Harlem or Southside Chicago. They turn into prostitutes, welfare cases, or outright derelicts. One tall, dark, tough-faced girl of about twenty-two, stated:

. . . damn white folks up here act just like the crackers down South. They want you to cook, wash, be a mammy, and fuck 'em too. The hell wit it—I'll carry my black butt back to Georgia first. At least down there I know where I stand.

On the other hand, the Negro woman may "take advantage" of the situation. Like any other woman, the black woman may "play along" with white men to obtain money, employment, and other "gains." But especially in the South (the North notwithstanding), much more is usually involved than mere "playing along." The white man, according to the overt mores of the South, is taboo as a husband for a black woman. A tension is therefore set up in the Negro woman when she is in his presence. She experiences temptation for the forbidden. Moreover, there is a more human element that tends to draw the Negro woman towards the white man. She works with and handles objects that are his personal possessions. She nurses his children, cooks his food, darns his socks, washes his underwear, and spends long hours in his home. In a laundry or a restaurant, too, the Negro woman works *around* white men, or she works with things that belong to the white man's *person*. A kind of symbolic or vicarious intimacy ensues which may create an unconscious desire in the black woman to actually experience the white man—and, despite her seemingly negative attitude, she may be waiting and hoping for his advance. Sexual contact with the white man may represent a way of "getting back" at his wife, or at white women in general. Dollard reports that a Negro woman informed him that one of her friends "slept in the very bed of the white man's wife without the wife's knowledge." He further stated that there may be the feeling of pulling the white man down, making him "come off his high perch," and showing him to be, after all, just another human being.[6]

More than once I have overheard Negro women in the South boasting among themselves about how well such and such a white man treats them, or about how they have secretly "wedded" such and such a white man to their apron strings, more securely than the man's own wife. And they laugh about it mockingly. For the Negro woman is aware that the white man believes that all Negro women are great sexual animals who can not only satisfy him better than any white woman but also who can release him from whatever complexes that may be repressing his sexuality. The white Southerner may treat Negroes with the utmost contempt in public, but the Negro woman knows the difference between the public white man and the private white man. Then, too, there is not a "good-looking" Negro woman in the South who has not been sexually approached by a white man.

6. John Dollard, *Caste and Class in a Southern Town* (Garden City, New York: Doubleday Anchor Books, 1949), p. 153.

6

"Blood-Burning Moon"

by Jean Toomer
(First published 1923)

FROM

Cane

Occasionally by consent, but most often by coercion, black women became sexually involved with white men. Since it was rare that these affairs were legalized or that black women were accepted by the white community, they usually continued to live among and have relationships with black men. Therefore their black and white suitors often became rivals. The conflicts that ensued sometimes progressed to violent clashes in which, almost certainly, the black male and often the black woman became the victims of the white men's retribution.

Jean Toomer (1894–1967) dramatized this classic conflict in the excerpt from his novel which follows. One witnesses the dilemma of the black man vying with a white man for a black woman, and sees the inevitable conclusion and the burden of responsibility bequeathed to the black woman.

1.

Up from the skeleton stone walls, up from the rotting floor boards and the solid hand-hewn beams of oak of the pre-war cotton factory, dusk came. Up from the dusk the full moon came. Glowing like a fired pine-knot, it illumined the great door and soft showed the Negro shanties aligned along the single street of factory town. The full moon in the great door was an omen. Negro women improvised songs against its spell.

Louisa sang as she came over the crest of the hill from the white folks' kitchen. Her skin was the color of oak leaves on young trees in fall. Her breasts, firm and up-pointed like ripe acorns. And her singing had the low murmur of winds in fig trees. Bob Stone, younger son of the people she worked for, loved her. By the way the world reckons things, he had won her. By measure of that warm glow which came into her mind at thought of him, he had won her. Tom Burwell, whom the whole town called Big Boy, also loved her. But working in the fields all day, and far away from her, gave him no chance to show it. Though often enough of evenings he had tried to. Somehow, he never got along. Strong as he was with his hands upon the ax or plow, he found it difficult to hold her. Or so he thought. But the fact was that he held her to factory town more firmly than he thought, for his black balanced, and pulled against, the white of Stone, when she thought of them. And her mind was vaguely upon them as she came over the crest of the hill, coming from the white folks' kitchen. As she sang softly at the evil face of the full moon.

A strange stir was in her. Indolently, she tried to fix upon Bob or Tom as the cause of it. To meet Bob in the canebrake, as she was going to do an hour or so later, was nothing new. And Tom's proposal which she felt on its way to her could be indefinitely put off. Separately, there was no unusual significance to either one. But for some reason, they jumbled when her eyes gazed vacantly at the rising moon. And from the jumble came the stir that was strangely within her. Her lips trembled. The slow rhythm of her song grew agitant and restless. Rusty black and tan spotted hounds, lying in the dark corners of porches or prowling around back yards, put their noses in the air and caught its tremor. They began plaintively to yelp and howl. Chickens woke up and cackled. Intermittently, all over the countryside dogs barked and roosters crowed as if heralding a weird dawn or some ungodly awakening. The women sang lustily. Their songs were cotton-wads to stop their ears. Louisa came down into factory town and sank wearily upon the step before her home. The moon was rising towards a thick cloud-bank which soon would hide it.

> Red nigger moon. Sinner!
> Blood-burning moon. Sinner!
> Come out that fact'ry door.

2.

Up from the deep dusk of a cleared spot on the edge of the forest a mellow glow arose and spread fan-wise into the low-hanging heavens. And all around the air was heavy with the scent of boiling cane. A large pile of cane-stalks lay like ribboned shadows upon the ground. A mule, harnessed to a pole, trudged lazily round and round the pivot of the grinder. Beneath a swaying oil lamp, a Negro alternately whipped out at the mule, and fed cane-stalks to the grinder. A fat boy waddled pails of fresh-ground juice between the grinder and the boiling stove. Steam came from the copper boiling pan. The scent of cane came from the copper pan and drenched the forest and the hill that sloped to factory town, beneath its fragrance. It drenched the men in the circle seated around the stove. Some of them chewed at the white pulp of stalks, but there was no need for them to, if all they wanted was to taste the cane. One tasted it in factory town. And from factory town one could see the soft haze thrown by the glowing stove upon the low-hanging heavens.

Old David Georgia stirred the thickening syrup with a long ladle, and ever so often drew it off. Old David Georgia tended his stove and told tales about the white folks, about moon-shining and cotton picking, and about sweet nigger gals, to the men who sat there about his stove to listen to him. Tom

Burwell chewed cane-stalk and laughed with the others till someone mentioned Louisa. Till someone said something about Louisa and Bob Stone, about the silk stockings she must have gotten from him. Blood ran up Tom's neck hotter than the glow that flooded from the stove. He sprang up. Glared at the men and said, "She's my gal." Will Manning laughed. Tom strode over to him. Yanked him up and knocked him to the ground. Several of Manning's friends got up to fight for him. Tom whipped out a long knife and would have cut them to shreds if they hadn't ducked into the woods. Tom had had enough. He nodded to Old David Georgia and swung down the path to factory town. Just then, the dogs started barking and the roosters began to crow. Tom felt funny. Away from the fight, away from the stove, chill got to him. He shivered. He shuddered when he saw the full moon rising towards the cloud-bank. He who didn't give a godam for the fears of old women. He forced his mind to fasten on Louisa. Bob Stone. Better not be. He turned into the street and saw Louisa sitting before her home. He went towards her, ambling, touched the brim of a marvelously shaped, spotted, felt hat, said he wanted to say something to her, and then found that he didn't know what he had to say, or if he did, that he couldn't say it. He shoved his big fists in his overalls, grinned, and started to move off.

"Youall want me, Tom?"

"Thats what us wants, sho, Louisa."

"Well, here I am—"

"An here I is, but that aint ahelpin none, all th same."

"You wanted to say somthing?"

"I did that, sho. But the words is like th spots on dice: no matter how y fumbles em, there's times when they jes wont come. I dunno why. Seems like th love I feels fo yo done stole m tongue. I got it now. Whee! Louisa, honey, I oughtnt tell y, I feel I oughtnt, cause yo is young an goes t church an I has had other gals, but Louisa I sho do love y. Lil gal, Ise watched y from them first days when youall sat right there befo yo door befo th well an sang sometimes in a way that like t broke m heart. Ise carried y with me into th fields, day after day, and after that, an I sho can plow when yo is there, an I can pick cotton. Yassur! Come near beatin Barlo yesterday. I sho did. Yassur! An next year if ole Stone'll trust me, I'll have a farm. My own. My bales will buy yo what y gets from white folks now. Silk stockings an purple dresses—course I dont believe what some folks been whisperin as t how y gets them things now. White folks always did do for niggers what they likes. An they jes cant help alikin yo, Louisa. Bob Stone likes y. Course he does. But not th way folks is awhisperin. Do he, hon?"

"I don't know what you mean, Tom."

"Course y dont. Ise already cut two niggers. Had to hon, to tell em so. Niggers always trying to make somethin outa nothin. An then besides, white folks aint up t them tricks so much nowadays. Godam—better not be. Leastawise not with you. Cause I wouldnt stand f it. Nassur."

"What would you do, Tom?"

"Cut him jes like I cut a nigger."

"No, Tom—"

"I said I would an there aint no mo to it. But that aint th talk f now. Sing, honey Louisa, an while I'm listenin t y I'll be makin love."

Tom took her hand in his. Against the tough thickness of his own, hers felt soft and small. His huge body slipped down to the step beside her. The full moon sank upward into the deep purple of the cloud-bank. An old woman brought a lighted lamp and hung it on the common well whose bulky shadow squatted in the middle of the road, opposite Tom and Louisa. The old woman lifted the well-lid, took hold the chain, and began drawing up the heavy bucket. As she did so, she sang. Figures shifted, restless-like, between lamp and window in the front rooms of the shanties. Shadows of the figures fought each other on the gray dust of the road. Figures

raised the windows and joined the old woman in song. Louisa
and Tom, the whole street, singing:

> Red nigger moon. Sinner!
> Blood-burning moon. Sinner!
> Come out that fact'ry door.

3.

Bob Stone sauntered from his veranda out into the gloom of
fir trees and magnolias. The clear white of his skin paled, and
the flush of his cheeks turned purple. As if to balance this
outer change, his mind became consciously a white man's. He
passed the house with its huge open hearth which, in the days
of slavery, was the plantation cookery. He saw Louisa bent
over that hearth. He went in as a master should and took her.
Direct, honest, bold. None of this sneaking that he had to
go through now. The contrast was repulsive to him. His family had lost ground. Hell no, his family still owned the niggers, practically. Damned if they did, or he wouldnt have to
duck around so. What would they think if they knew? His
mother? His sister? He shouldnt mention them, shouldnt
think of them in this connection. There in the dark he
blushed at doing so. Fellows about town were all right, but
how about his friends up North? He could see them, incredulous, repulsed. They didnt know. The thought first made
him laugh. Then, with their eyes still upon him, he began to
feel embarrassed. He felt the need of explaining things to
them. Explain hell. They wouldnt understand, and moreover,
who ever heard of a Southerner getting on his knees to any
Yankee, or anyone. No sir. He was going to see Louisa tonight, and love her. She was lovely—in her way. Nigger way.
What way was that? Damned if he knew. Must know. He'd
known her long enough to know. Was there something about
niggers that you couldnt know? Listening to them at church
didnt tell you anything. Looking at them didnt tell you anything. Talking to them didnt tell you anything—unless it was

gossip, unless they wanted to talk. Of course, about farming, and licker, and craps—but those werent nigger. Nigger was something more. How much more? Something to be afraid of, more? Hell no. Who ever heard of being afraid of a nigger? Tom Burwell. Cartwell had told him that Tom went with Louisa after she reached home. No sir. No nigger had ever been with his girl. He'd like to see one try. Some position for him to be in. Him, Bob Stone, of the Stone family, in a scrap with a nigger over a nigger girl. In the good old days . . . Ha! Those were the days. His family had lost ground. Not so much, though. Enough for him to have to cut through old Lemon's canefield by way of the woods, that he might meet her. She was worth it. Beautiful nigger gal. Why nigger? Why not, just gal? No, it was because she was nigger that he went to her. Sweet . . . The scent of boiling cane came to him. Then he saw the rich glow of the stove. He heard the voices of the men circled around it. He was about to skirt the clearing when he heard his own name mentioned. He stopped. Quivering. Leaning against a tree, he listened.

"Bad nigger. Yassur, he sho is one bad nigger when he gets started."

"Tom Burwell's been on th gang three times fo cuttin men."

"What y think he's a gwine to do t Bob Stone?"

"Dunno yet. He aint found out. When he does—Baby!"

"Young Stone aint no quitter an I ken tell y that. Blood of th old uns in his veins."

"That's right. He'll scrap, sho."

"Be gettin too hot f niggers round this away."

"Shut up, nigger. Y dont know what y talkin bout."

Bob Stone's ears burned as though he had been holding them over the stove. Sizzling heat welled up within him. His feet felt as if they rested on red-hot coals. They stung him to quick movement. He circled the fringe of the glowing. Not a twig cracked beneath his feet. He reached the path that led to factory town. Plunged furiously down it. Halfway along, a blindness within him veered him aside. He crashed into the bordering canebrake. Cane leaves cut his face and lips. He tasted blood. He threw himself down and dug his fingers in the ground. The earth was cool. Cane-roots took the fever from his hands. After a long while, or so it seemed to him, the thought came to him that it must be time to see Louisa. He got to his feet and walked calmly to their meeting place. No Louisa. Tom Burwell had her. Veins in his forehead bulged and distended. Saliva moistened the dried blood on his lips. He bit down on his lips. He tasted blood. Not his own blood; Tom Burwell's blood. Bob drove through the cane and out again upon the road. A hound swung down the path before him towards factory town. Bob couldn't see it. The dog loped aside to let him pass. Bob's blind rushing made him stumble over it. He fell with a thud that dazed him. The hound yelped. Answering yelps came from all over the countryside. Chickens cackled. Roosters crowed, heralding the bloodshot eyes of southern awakening. Singers in the town were silenced. They shut their windows down. Palpitant between the rooster crows, a chill hush settled upon the huddled forms of Tom and Louisa. A figure rushed from the shadow and stood before them. Tom popped to his feet.

"Whats y want?"

"I'm Bob Stone."

"Yassur—and I'm Tom Burwell. Whats y want?"

Bob lunged at him. Tom side-stepped, caught him by the shoulder, and flung him to the ground. Straddled him.

"Let me up."

"Yassur—but watch yo doins, Bob Stone."

A few dark figures, drawn by the sound of scuffle, stood about them. Bob sprang to his feet.

"Fight like a man, Tom Burwell, an I'll lick y."

Again he lunged. Tom side-stepped and flung him to the ground. Straddled him.

"Get off me, you godam nigger you."

"Yo sho has started somethin now. Get up."

Tom yanked him up and began hammering at him. Each blow sounded as if it smashed into a precious, irreplaceable soft something. Beneath them, Bob staggered back. He reached in his pocket and whipped out a knife. "That's my game, sho."

Blue flash, a steel blade slashed across Bob Stone's throat. He had a sweetish sick feeling. Blood began to flow. Then he felt a sharp twitch of pain. He let his knife drop. He slapped one hand against his neck. He pressed the other on top of his head as if to hold it down. He groaned. He turned, and staggered towards the crest of the hill in the direction of white town. Negroes who had seen the fight slunk into their homes and blew the lamps out. Louisa, dazed, hysterical, refused to go indoors. She slipped, crumpled, her body loosely propped against the woodwork of the well. Tom Burwell leaned against it. He seemed rooted there.

Bob reached Broad Street. White men rushed up to him. He collapsed in their arms.

"Tom Burwell. . . ."

White men like ants upon a forage rushed about. Except for the taut hum of their moving, all was silent. Shotguns, revolvers, rope, kerosene, torches. Two high-powered cars with glaring search-lights. They came together. The taut hum rose to a low roar. Then nothing could be heard but the flop of their feet in the thick dust of the road. The moving body of their silence preceded them over the crest of the hill into factory town. It flattened the Negroes beneath it. It rolled to the wall of the factory, where it stopped. Tom knew that they were coming. He couldn't move. And then he saw the search-lights of the two cars glaring down on him. A quick shock went through him. He stiffened. He started to run. A yell went up from the mob. Tom wheeled about and faced them. They poured down on him. They swarmed. A large man with dead-white face and flabby cheeks came to him and almost jabbed a gun-barrel through his guts.

"Hands behind y, nigger."

Tom's wrists were bound. The big man shoved him to the well. Burn him over it, and when the woodwork caved in, his body would drop to the bottom. Two deaths for a godam nigger.

Louisa was driven back. The mob pushed in. Its pressure, its momentum was too great. Drag him to the factory. Wood and stakes already there. Tom moved in the direction indicated. But they had to drag him. They reached the great door. Too many to get in there. The mob divided and flowed around the walls to either side. The big man shoved him through the door. The mob pressed in from the sides. Taut humming. No words. A stake was sunk into the ground. Rotting floor boards piled around it. Kerosene poured on the rotting floor boards. Tom bound to the stake. His breast was bare. Nails scratches let little lines of blood trickle down and mat into the hair. His face, his eyes were set and stony. Except for irregular breathing, one would have thought him already dead. Torches were flung onto the pile. A great flare muffled in black smoke shot upward. The mob yelled. The mob was silent. Now Tom could be seen within the flames. Only his head, erect, lean, like a blackened stone. Stench of burning flesh soaked the air. Tom's eyes popped. His head settled downward. The mob yelled. Its yell echoed against the skeleton stone walls and sounded like a hundred yells. Like a hundred mobs yelling. Its yell thudded against the thick front wall and fell back. Ghost of a yell slipped through the flames and out the great door of the factory. It fluttered like a dying thing down the single street of factory town. Louisa, upon the step before her home, did not hear it, but her eyes opened slowly. They saw the full moon glowing in the great door. The full moon, an evil thing, an omen, soft showering the homes of folks she knew. Where were they, these people? She'd sing, and perhaps they'd come out and join her. Perhaps Tom Burwell would come. At any rate, the full moon in the great door was an omen which she must sing to:

> Red nigger moon. Sinner!
> Blood-burning moon. Sinner!
> Come out that fact'ry door.

7

FROM

In White America

by Martin B. Duberman
(First produced 1963)

The abuses of racial discrimination are also felt in the black family. In most instances it is the mother who prepares her children for the experiences that await them in the white world. The following selection from a "documentary play" by dramatist and essayist Martin B. Duberman shows the futility of one black mother's efforts, and dramatically recreates her young daughter's initial terror and her courage as she is personally confronted by American prejudice.

NARRATOR: *There was no major breakthrough [in the civil rights movement] until 1954, when the Supreme Court declared segregation in public schools unconstitutional. Southern resistance to the court's decision came to a head three years later at Little Rock, Arkansas, when a fifteen-year-old girl tried to go to school at Central High.*

GIRL: The night before I was so excited I couldn't sleep. The next morning I was about the first one up. While I was pressing my black and white dress—I had made it to wear on the first day of school—my little brother turned on the TV set. They started telling about a large crowd gathered at the school. The man on TV said he wondered if we were going to show up that morning. Mother called from the kitchen, where she was fixing breakfast, "Turn that TV off!" She was so upset and worried. I wanted to comfort her, so I said, "Mother, don't worry!"

Dad was walking back and forth, from room to room, with a sad expression. He was chewing on his pipe and he had a cigar in his hand, but he didn't light either one. It would have been funny, only he was so nervous.

Before I left home Mother called us into the living room. She said we should have a word of prayer. Then I caught the bus and got off a block from the school. I saw a large crowd of people standing across the street from the soldiers guarding Central. As I walked on, the crowd suddenly got very quiet. For a moment all I could hear was the shuffling of their feet. Then someone shouted, "Here she comes, get ready!" The crowd moved in closer and then began to follow me, calling me names. I still wasn't afraid. Just a little bit nervous. Then my knees started to shake all of a sudden and I wondered whether I could make it to the center entrance a block away. It was the longest block I ever walked in my whole life.

Even so, I still wasn't too scared because all the time I kept thinking that the guards would protect me.

When I got right in front of the school, I went up to a guard. He just looked straight ahead and didn't move to let me pass him. I stood looking at the school—it looked so big! Just then the guards let some white students go through.

The crowd was quiet. I guess they were waiting to see what was going to happen. When I was able to steady my knees, I walked up to the guard who had let the white students in. He too didn't move. When I tried to squeeze past him, he raised his bayonet and then the other guards closed in and they raised their bayonets.

They glared at me with a mean look and I was very frightened and didn't know what to do. I turned around and the crowd came toward me. They moved closer and closer. Somebody started yelling, "Lynch her!" "Lynch her!"

I tried to see a friendly face somewhere in the mob—someone who maybe would help. I looked into the face of an old woman and it seemed a kind face, but when I looked at her again, she spat on me.

They came closer, shouting, "No nigger bitch is going to get in our school. Get out of here!" Then I looked down the block and saw a bench at the bus stop. I thought, "If I can only get there I will be safe." I don't know why the bench seemed a safe place to me, but I started walking toward it. I tried to close my mind to what they were shouting, and kept saying to myself, "If I can only make it to the bench I will be safe."

When I finally got there, I don't think I could have gone another step. I sat down and the mob crowded up and began shouting all over again. Someone hollered, "Drag her over to this tree! Let's take care of the nigger." Just then a white man sat down beside me, put his arm around me and patted my shoulder.

(During last part of speech, white actor sits beside her on bench.)

WHITE MAN: She just sat there, her head down. Tears were streaming down her cheeks. I don't know what made me put my arm around her, saying, "Don't let them see you cry." Maybe she reminded me of my 15-year-old daughter. Just then the city bus came and she got on. She must have been in a state of shock. She never uttered a word.

GIRL: I can't remember much about the bus ride, but the next thing I remember I was standing in front of the

School for the Blind, where Mother works. I ran upstairs and I kept running until I reached Mother's classroom.

Mother was standing at the window with her head bowed, but she must have sensed I was there because she turned around. She looked as if she had been crying, and I wanted to tell her I was all right. But I couldn't speak. She put her arms around me and I cried.

11

BLACK ON WHITE

THE BLACK WOMAN
IN THE WHITE WORLD

SINCE arriving in America, black people have led a dual existence; their daily lives have been split between distinctly different black and white worlds. They have usually played, socialized, loved, worshipped, and lived in black communities where the appearance of a white person—except for shop-owners, insurance men, welfare workers, or bill collectors—was rare. But "going to meet the man" has also been a necessary, if generally abusive, part of their daily lives.

Traditionally, black women have had more contact with the white world than black men. During slavery the various roles the black woman was forced to assume often placed her in intimate contact with whites. She was not only more likely to have worked in the slave master's house as a cook or maid, but also reared his wife's children and, on occasion, served as her master's concubine. Later, she found it both necessary and easier than the black male to obtain a job with white employers. From this continued contact as servant, always affected by the recognition that she was fair game for the white world's exploitation, was shaped many of the black woman's attitudes.

The excerpts that follow, some from famous black female personalities, graphically explore the problems of the black woman relating to a world that insults her, denies her femininity, yet craves her sexually. The more complex problem of a dignified relationship between the black woman and the white male also emerges in the selections by Lena Horne and James Baldwin.

1

"The Ethics of Living Jim Crow"

by Richard Wright
(First published 1940)

FROM
Uncle Tom's Children

As a domestic or servant, the black woman was subject to both the contempt and lust of white men. In the following excerpt from his autobiographical account of growing up in Mississippi, Richard Wright evocatively demonstrates the insults the black woman had to bear and, also, the black male's inability to protect either himself or his woman from the oppression of the white world.

ONE NIGHT just as I was about to go home, I met one of the Negro maids. She lived in my direction, and we fell in to walk part of the way home together. As we passed the white night-watchman, he slapped the maid on her buttock. I turned around, amazed. The watchman looked at me with a long, hard, fixed-under stare. Suddenly he pulled his gun and asked:

"Nigger, don't yuh like it?"

I hesitated.

"I asked yuh don't yuh like it?" he asked again, stepping forward.

"Yes, sir," I mumbled.

"Talk like it, then!"

"Oh, yes, sir!" I said with as much heartiness as I could muster.

Outside, I walked ahead of the girl, ashamed to face her. She caught up with me and said:

"Don't be a fool! Yuh couldn't help it!"

This watchman boasted of having killed two Negroes in self-defense.

Yet, in spite of all this, the life of the hotel ran with an amazing smoothness. It would have been impossible for a stranger to detect anything. The maids, the hall-boys, and the bell-boys were all smiles. They had to be.

2

"Health Card"

by Frank Yerby
(First published 1944)

FROM

The Best Short Stories by Negro Writers
edited by Langston Hughes

*The male's impotence in the outside world has always been
the most destructive element in black male-female relationships. During slavery a black woman could literally be taken
from the arms of her black lover and forced to submit to her
white master. Although after slavery was abolished the means
of emasculating black men became more subtle, the result
was no less destructive. This early short story by Frank Yerby,
a Georgia-born writer whose later novels sold over two million copies, vividly illustrates the effect prejudice had on
black male-female relationships.*

JOHNNY stood under one of the street lights on the corner
and tried to read the letter. The street lights down in the
Bottom were so dim that he couldn't make out half the words,
but he didn't need to; he knew them all by heart anyway.

"Sugar," he read, "it took a long time but I done it. I got
the money to come to see you. I waited and waited for them
to give you a furlough, but it look like they don't mean to.
Sugar, I can't wait no longer. I got to see you. I got to. Find
a nice place for me to stay—where we can be happy together.
You know what I mean. With all my love, Lily."

Johnny folded the letter up and put it back in his pocket. Then he walked swiftly down the street past all the juke joints with the music blaring out and the G.I. brogans pounding. He turned down a side street, scuffing up a cloud of dust as he did so. None of the streets down in Black Bottom was paved, and there were four inches of fine white powder over everything. When it rained the mud would come up over the tops of his army shoes, but it hadn't rained in nearly three months. There were no juke joints on this street, and the Negro shanties were neatly whitewashed. Johnny kept on walking until he came to the end of the street. On the corner stood the little whitewashed Baptist Church, and next to it was the neat, well-kept home of the pastor.

Johnny went up on the porch and hesitated. He thrust his hand in his pocket and the paper crinkled. He took his hand out and knocked on the door.

"Who's that?" a voice called.

"It's me," Johnny answered, "it's a sodjer."

The door opened a crack and a woman peered out. She was middle-aged and fat. Looking down, Johnny could see that her feet were bare.

"Whatcha want, sodjer?"

Johnny took off his cap.

"Please, ma'am, lemme come in. I kin explain it t' yuh better settin' down."

She studied his face for a minute in the darkness.

"Aw right," she said; "you kin come in, son."

Johnny entered the room stiffly and sat down on a corn-shuck-bottomed chair.

"It's this way, ma'am," he said. "I got a wife up Nawth. I been tryin' an' tryin' t' git a furlough so I could go t' see huh. But they always put me off. So now she done worked an' saved enuff money t' come an' see me. I wants t' ax you t' rent me a room, ma'am. I doan' know nowheres t' ax."

"This ain't no hotel, son."

"I know it ain't. I cain't take Lily t' no hotel, not lak hotels in this heah town."

"Lily yo wife?"

"Yes'm. She my sho' nuff, honest t' Gawd wife. Married in th' Baptist Church in Deetroit."

The fat woman sat back, and her thick lips widened into a smile.

"She a good girl, ain't she? An' you doan' wanta take her t' one o' these heah ho'houses they calls hotels."

"That's it, ma'am."

"Sho' you kin bring huh heah, son. Be glad t' have huh. Reveren' be glad t' have huh too. What yo, name, son?"

"Johnny. Johnny Green. Ma'am—"

"Yas, son?"

"You understands that I wants t' come heah too?"

The fat woman rocked back in her chair and gurgled with laughter.

"Bless yo' heart, chile, I ain't always been a ole woman! And I ain't always been th' preacher's wife neither!"

"Thank you, ma'am. I gotta go now. Time fur me t' be getin' back t' camp."

"When you bring Lily?"

"Be Monday night, ma'am. Pays you now if you wants it."

"Monday be aw right. Talk it over with th' Reveren', so he make it light fur yuh. Know sodjer boys ain't got much money."

"No, ma'am, sho' Lawd ain't. G'night, ma'am."

When he turned back into the main street of the Negro section the doors of the joints were all open and the soldiers were coming out. The girls were clinging onto their arms all the way to the bus stop. Johnny looked at the dresses that stopped halfway between the pelvis and the knee and hugged the backside so that every muscle showed when they walked. He saw the purple lipstick smeared across the wide full lips, and the short hair stiffened with smelly grease so that it covered their heads like a black lacquered cap. They went on down to the bus stop arm in arm, their knotty bare calves bunching with each step as they walked. Johnny thought about Lily. He walked past them very fast without turning his head.

But just as he reached the bus stop he heard the whistles. When he turned around he saw the four M.P.s and the civilian policeman stopping the crowd. He turned around again and walked back until he was standing just behind the white men.

"Aw right," the M.P.s were saying, "you gals git your health cards out."

Some of the girls started digging in their handbags. Johnny could see them dragging out small yellow cardboard squares. But the others just stood there with blank expressions on their faces. The soldiers started muttering, a dark, deep-throated sound. The M.P.s started pushing their way through the crowd, looking at each girl's card as they passed. When they came to a girl who didn't have a card they called out to the civilian policemen:

"Aw right, mister, take A'nt Jemina for a little ride."

Then the city policemen would lead the girl away and put her in the Black Maria.

They kept this up until they had examined every girl except one. She hung back beside her soldier, and the first time the M.P.s didn't see her. When they came back through, one of them caught her by the arm.

"Lemme see your card, Mandy," he said.

The girl looked at him, her little eyes narrowing into slits in her black face.

"Tek yo' hands offen me, white man," she said.

The M.P.'s face crimsoned, so that Johnny could see it, even in the darkness.

"Listen, black girl," he said, "I told you to lemme see your card."

"An I tole you t' tek yo' han' offen me, white man!"

"Gawddammit, you little black bitch, you better do like I tell you."

Johnny didn't see very clearly what happened after that. There was a sudden explosion of motion, and then the M.P. was trying to jerk his hand back, but he couldn't, for the little black girl had it between her teeth and was biting it to the bone. He drew his other hand back and slapped her across the face so hard that it sounded like a pistol shot. She went over backwards and her tight skirt split, so that when she got up Johnny could see that she didn't have anything on under it. She came forward like a cat, her nails bared, straight for the M.P.'s eyes. He slapped her down again, but the soldiers surged forward all at once. The M.P.s fell back and drew their guns and one of them blew a whistle.

Johnny, who was behind them, decided it was time for him to get out of there and he did; but not before he saw the squads of white M.P.s hurtling around the corner and going to work on the Negroes with their clubs. He reached the bus stop and swung on board. The minute after he had pushed his way to the back behind all the white soldiers he heard the shots. The bus driver put the bus in gear and they roared off toward the camp.

It was after one o'clock when all the soldiers straggled in. Those of them who could still walk. Eight of them came in on the meat wagon, three with gunshot wounds. The colonel declared the town out of bounds for all Negro soldiers for a month.

"Dammit," Johnny said, "I gotta go meet Lily, I gotta. I cain't stay heah. I cain't!"

"Whatcha gonna do," Little Willie asked, "go A.W.O.L.?"

Johnny looked at him, his brow furrowed into a frown.

"Naw," he said, "I'm gonna go see th' colonel!"

"Whut! Man, you crazy! Colonel kick yo' black ass out fo' you gits yo' mouf open."

"I take a chanct on that."

He walked over to the little half mirror on the wall of the

barracks. Carefully he readjusted his cap. He pulled his tie out of his shirt front and drew the knot tighter around his throat. Then he tucked the ends back in at just the right fraction of an inch between the correct pair of buttons. He bent down and dusted his shoes again, although they were already spotless.

"Man," Little Willie said, "you sho' is a fool!"

"Reckon I am," Johnny said; then he went out of the door and down the short wooden steps.

When he got to the road that divided the colored and white sections of the camp his steps faltered. He stood still a minute, drew in a deep breath, and marched very stiffly and erect across the road. The white soldiers gazed at him curiously, but none of them said anything. If a black soldier came over into their section it was because somebody sent him, so they let him alone.

In front of the colonel's headquarters he stopped. He knew what he had to say, but his breath was very short in his throat and he was going to have a hard time saying it.

"Whatcha want, soldier?" the sentry demanded.

"I wants t' see th' colonel."

"Who sent you?"

Johnny drew his breath in sharply.

"I ain't at liberty t' say," he declared, his breath coming out very fast behind the words.

"You ain't at liberty t' say," the sentry mimicked. "Well I'll be damned! If you ain't at liberty t' say, then I ain't at liberty t' let you see the colonel! Git tha hell outa here, nigger, before I pump some lead in you!"

Johnny didn't move.

The sentry started toward him, lifting his rifle butt, but another soldier, a sergeant, came around the corner of the building.

"Hold on there," he called. "What tha hell is th' trouble here?"

"This here nigger says he want t' see tha colonel an' when I ast him who sent him he says he ain't at liberty t' say!"

The sergeant turned to Johnny.

Johnny came to attention and saluted him. You aren't supposed to salute N.C.O.s, but sometimes it helps.

"What you got t' say fur yourself, boy?" the sergeant said, not unkindly. Johnny's breath evened.

"I got uh message fur th' colonel, suh," he said; "I ain't s'posed t' give it t' nobody else but him. I ain't even s'posed t' tell who sont it, suh."

The sergeant peered at him sharply.

"You tellin' tha truth, boy?"

"Yassuh!"

"Aw right. Wait here a minute."

He went into H.Q. After a couple of minutes he came back.

"Aw right, soldier, you kin go on in."

Johnny mounted the steps and went into the colonel's office. The colonel was a lean, white-haired soldier with a face tanned to the color of saddle leather. He was reading a letter through a pair of horn-rimmed glasses which had only one earhook left, so that he had to hold them up to his eyes with one hand. He put them down and looked up. Johnny saw that his eyes were pale blue, so pale that he felt as if he were looking into the eyes of an eagle or some other fierce bird of prey.

"Well?" he said, and Johnny stiffened into a salute. The colonel half smiled.

"At ease, soldier," he said. Then: "The sergeant tells me that you have a very important message for me."

Johnny gulped in the air.

"Beggin' th' sergeant's pardon, suh," he said, "but that ain't so."

"What!"

"Yassuh," Johnny rushed on, "nobody sent me. I come on m' own hook. I had t' talk t' yuh, Colonel, suh! You kin sen' me t' th' guardhouse afterwards, but please, suh, lissen t' me fur jes' a minute!"

The colonel relaxed slowly. Something very like a smile was playing around the corners of his mouth. He looked at his watch.

"All right, soldier," he said. "You've got five minutes."

"Thank yuh, thank yuh, suh!"

"Speak your piece, soldier; you're wasting time!"

"It's about Lily, suh. She my wife. She done worked an' slaved fur nigh onto six months t' git the money t' come an' see me. An' now you give th' order that none of th' cullud boys kin go t' town. Beggin' yo' pahdon, suh, I wasn't in none of that trouble. I ain't neber been in no trouble. You kin ax my cap'n, if you wants to. All I wants is permission to go into town fur one week, an' I'll stay outa town fur two months if yuh wants me to."

The colonel picked up the phone.

"Ring Captain Walters for me," he said. Then: "What's your name, soldier?"

"It's Green, suh. Private Johnny Green."

"Captain Walters? This is Colonel Milton. Do you have anything in your files concerning Private Johnny Green? Oh yes, go ahead. Take all the time you need."

The colonel lit a long black cigar. Johnny waited. The clock on the wall spun its electric arms.

"What's that? Yes. Yes, yes, I see. Thank you, Captain."

He put down the phone and picked up a fountain pen. He wrote swiftly. Finally he straightened up and gave Johnny the slip of paper.

Johnny read it. It said: "Private Johnny Green is given express permission to go into town every evening of the week beginning August seventh and ending August fourteenth. He is further permitted to remain in town overnight every night during said week, so long as he returns to camp for reveille the following morning. By order of the commanding officer, Colonel H. H. Milton."

There was a hard knot at the base of Johnny's throat. He couldn't breathe. But he snapped to attention and saluted smartly.

"Thank yuh, suh," he said at last. Then: "Gawd bless you, suh!"

"Forget it, soldier. I was a young married man once myself. My compliments to Captain Walters."

Johnny saluted again and about-faced, then he marched out of the office and down the stairs. On the way back he saluted everybody—privates, N.C.O.s, and civilian visitors, his white teeth gleaming in a huge smile.

"That's sure one happy darky," one of the white soldiers said.

Johnny stood in the station and watched the train running in. The yellow lights from the windows flickered on and off across his face as the alternating squares of light and darkness flashed past. Then it was slowing and Johnny was running beside it, trying to keep abreast of the Jim Crow coach. He could see her standing up, holding her bags. She came down the steps the first one and they stood there holding each other, Johnny's arms crushing all the breath out of her, holding her so hard against him that his brass buttons hurt through her thin dress. She opened her mouth to speak but he kissed her, bending her head backward on her neck until her little hat fell off. It lay there on the ground, unnoticed.

"Sugah," she said, "sugah. It was awful."

"I know," he said. "I know."

Then he took her bags and they started walking out of the station toward the Negro section of town.

"I missed yuh so much," Johnny said, "I thought I lose m' mind."

"Me too," she said. Then: "I brought th' marriage license with me like yuh tole me. I doan' wan th' preacher's wife t' think we bad."

"Enybody kin look at yuh an' see yuh uh angel!"

They went very quietly through all the dark streets and the white soldiers turned to look at Johnny and his girl.

Lak a queen, Johnny thought, lak a queen. He looked at the girl beside him, seeing the velvety nightshade skin, the glossy black lacquered curls, the sweet, wide hips and the long, clean legs striding beside him in the darkness. I am black, but comely, O ye daughters of Jerusalem!

They turned into the Bottom where the street lights were dim blobs on the pine poles and the dust rose up in little swirls around their feet. Johnny had his head half turned so that he didn't see the two M.P.s until he had almost bumped into them. He dropped one bag and caught Lily by the arm. Then he drew her aside quickly and the two men went by them without speaking.

They kept on walking, but every two steps Johnny would jerk his head around and look nervously back over his shoulder. The last time he looked the two M.P.s had stopped and were looking back at them. Johnny turned out the elbow of the arm next to Lily so that it hooked into hers a little and began to walk faster, pushing her along with him.

"What's yo' hurry, sugah?" she said. "I be heah a whole week!"

But Johnny was looking over his shoulder at the two M.P.s. They were coming toward them now, walking with long, slow strides, their reddish-white faces set. Johnny started to push Lily along faster, but she shook off his arm and stopped still.

"I do declare, Johnny Green! You th' beatines' man! Whut you walk me so fas' fur?"

Johnny opened his mouth to answer her, but the military police were just behind them now, and the sergeant reached out and laid his hand on her arm.

"C'mon, gal," he said, "lemme see it."

"Let you see whut? Whut he mean, Johnny?"

"Your card," the sergeant growled. "Lemme see your card."

"My card?" Lily said blankly. "Whut kinda card, mister?"

Johnny put the bags down. He was fighting for breath.

"Look heah, Sarge," he said; "this girl my wife!"

"Oh yeah? I said lemme see your card, sister!"

"I ain't got no card, mister. I dunno whut you talkin' about."

"Look, Sarge," the other M.P. said, "th' soldier's got bags. Maybe she's just come t' town."

"These your bags, gal?"

"Yessir."

"Aw right. You got twenty-four hours to git yourself a health card. If you don't have it by then we hafta run you in. Git goin' now."

"Listen," Johnny shouted; "this girl my wife! She ain't no ho'! I tell you she ain't—"

"What you say, nigger—" the M.P. sergeant growled. "Whatcha say?" He started toward Johnny.

Lily swung on Johnny's arm.

"C'mon, Johnny," she said; "they got guns. C'mon, Johnny, please! Please, Johnny!"

Slowly she drew him away.

"Aw, leave 'em be, Sarge," the M.P. corporal said; "maybe she is his wife."

The sergeant spat. The brown tobacco juice splashed in the dirt not an inch from Lily's foot. Then the two of them turned and started away.

Johnny stopped.

"Lemme go, Lily," he said, "lemme go!" He tore her arm loose from his and started back up the street. Lily leaped, her two arms fastening themselves around his neck. He fought silently but she clung to him, doubling her knees so that all her weight was hanging from his neck.

"No, Johnny! Oh Jesus no! You be kilt! Oh, Johnny, listen t' me, sugah! You's all I got!"

He put both hands up to break her grip but she swung her weight sidewise and the two of them went down in the dirt. The M.P.s turned the corner out of sight.

Johnny sat there in the dust staring at her. The dirt had

ruined her dress. He sat there a long time looking at her un-til the hot tears rose up back of his eyelids faster than he could blink them away, so he put his face down in her lap and cried.

"I ain't no man!" he said. "I ain't no man!"

"Hush, sugah," she said. "You's a man aw right. You's my man!"

Gently she drew him to his feet. He picked up the bags and the two of them went down the dark street toward the preach-er's house.

3

FROM

The Autobiography of Malcolm X

with the assistance of Alex Haley
(First published in 1964)

*As illustrated in the previous selections violence and the
threat of violence were frequently part of the black man's and
black woman's lives. However, racism was also expressed in
less obvious but no less wounding ways, as shown in this selection by Malcolm X, who describes the effect institutional-
ized racism had on his mother as she fought to keep her family together.*

ONE afternoon in 1931 when Wilfred, Hilda, Philbert, and
I came home, my mother and father were having one of their
arguments. There had lately been a lot of tension around the
house because of Black Legion threats. Anyway, my father
had taken one of the rabbits which we were raising, and ordered my mother to cook it. We raised rabbits, but sold them
to whites. My father had taken a rabbit from the rabbit pen.
He had pulled off the rabbit's head. He was so strong, he
needed no knife to behead chickens or rabbits. With one
twist of his big black hands he simply twisted off the head and
threw the bleeding-necked thing back at my mother's feet.

My mother was crying. She started to skin the rabbit, preparatory to cooking it. But my father was so angry he slammed
on out of the front door and started walking up the road toward town.

It was then that my mother had this vision. She had always

been a strange woman in this sense, and had always had a strong intuition of things about to happen. And most of her children are the same way, I think. When something is about to happen, I can feel something, sense something. I never have known something to happen that has caught me completely off guard—except once. And that was when, years later, I discovered facts I couldn't believe about a man who, up until that discovery, I would gladly have given my life for.

My father was well up the road when my mother ran screaming out onto the porch. *"Early! Early!"* She screamed his name. She clutched up her apron in one hand, and ran down across the yard and into the road. My father turned around. He saw her. For some reason, considering how angry he had been when he left, he waved at her. But he kept on going.

She told me later, my mother did, that she had a vision of my father's end. All the rest of the afternoon, she was not herself, crying and nervous and upset. She finished cooking the rabbit and put the whole thing in the warmer part of the black stove. When my father was not back home by our bedtime, my mother hugged and clutched us, and we felt strange, not knowing what to do, because she had never acted like that.

I remember waking up to the sound of my mother's screaming again. When I scrambled out, I saw the police in the living room; they were trying to calm her down. She had snatched on her clothes to go with them. And all of us children who were staring knew without anyone having to say it that something terrible had happened to our father.

My mother was taken by the police to the hospital, and to a room where a sheet was over my father in a bed, and she wouldn't look, she was afraid to look. Probably it was wise that she didn't. My father's skull, on one side, was crushed in, I was told later. Negroes in Lansing have always whispered that he was attacked, and then laid across some tracks for a streetcar to run over him. His body was cut almost in half.

He lived two and a half hours in that condition. Negroes then were stronger than they are now, especially Georgia Negroes. Negroes born in Georgia had to be strong simply to survive.

It was morning when we children at home got the word that he was dead. I was six. I can remember a vague commotion, the house filled up with people crying, saying bitterly that the white Black Legion had finally gotten him. My mother was hysterical. In the bedroom, women were holding smelling salts under her nose. She was still hysterical at the funeral. . . .

We children adjusted more easily than our mother did. We couldn't see, as clearly as she did, the trials that lay ahead. As the visitors tapered off, she became very concerned about collecting the two insurance policies that my father had always been proud he carried. He had always said that families should be protected in case of death. One policy apparently paid off without any problem—the smaller one. I don't know the amount of it. I would imagine it was not more than a thousand dollars, and maybe half of that.

But after that money came, and my mother had paid out a lot of it for the funeral and expenses, she began going into town and returning very upset. The company that had issued the bigger policy was balking at paying off. They were claiming that my father had committed suicide. Visitors came again, and there was bitter talk about white people: how could my father bash himself in the head, then get down across the streetcar tracks to be run over?

So there we were. My mother was thirty-four years old now, with no husband, no provider or protector to take care of her eight children. But some kind of a family routine got going again. And for as long as the first insurance money lasted, we did all right. . . .

My mother began to buy on credit. My father had always been very strongly against credit. "Credit is the first step into debt and back into slavery," he had always said. And then she went to work herself. She would go into Lansing and find different jobs—in housework, or sewing—for white people. They didn't realize, usually, that she was a Negro. A lot of white people around there didn't want Negroes in their houses.

She would do fine until in some way or other it got to people who she was. And then she would be let go. I remember how she used to come home crying, but trying to hide it, because she had lost a job that she needed so much.

Once when one of us—I cannot remember which—had to go for something to where she was working, and the people saw us, and realized she was actually a Negro, she was fired on the spot, and she came home crying, this time not hiding it.

When the state Welfare people began coming to our house, we would come from school sometimes and find them talking with our mother, asking a thousand questions. They acted and looked at her, and at us, and around in our house, in a way that had about it the feeling—at least for me—that we were not people. In their eyesight we were just *things,* that was all.

My mother began to receive two checks—a Welfare check and, I believe, a widow's pension. The checks helped. But they weren't enough, as many of us as there were. When they came, about the first of the month, one always was already owed in full, if not more, to the man at the grocery store. And, after that, the other one didn't last long.

We began to go swiftly downhill. The physical downhill wasn't as quick as the psychological. My mother was, above everything else, a proud woman, and it took its toll on her that she was accepting charity. And her feelings were communicated to us.

She would speak sharply to the man at the grocery store for padding the bill, telling him that she wasn't ignorant, and he didn't like that. She would talk back sharply to the state Welfare people, telling them that she was a grown woman, able to raise her children, that it wasn't necessary for them to keep coming around so much, meddling in our lives. And they didn't like that.

But the monthly Welfare check was their pass. They acted as if they owned us, as if we were their private property. As much as my mother would have liked to, she couldn't keep them out. She would get particularly incensed when they began insisting upon drawing us older children aside, one at a time, out on the porch or somewhere, and asking us questions, or telling us things—against our mother and against each other.

We couldn't understand why, if the state was willing to give us packages of meat, sacks of potatoes and fruit, and cans of all kinds of things, our mother obviously hated to accept. We really couldn't understand. What I later understood was that my mother was making a desperate effort to preserve her pride—and ours.

Pride was just about all we had to preserve, for by 1934, we really began to suffer. This was about the worst depression year, and no one we knew had enough to eat or live on. Some old family friends visited us now and then. At first they brought food. Though it was charity, my mother took it.

Wilfred was working to help. My mother was working, when she could find any kind of job. In Lansing, there was a bakery where, for a nickel, a couple of us children would buy a tall flour sack of day-old bread and cookies, and then walk the two miles back out into the country to our house. Our mother knew, I guess, dozens of ways to cook things with bread and out of bread. Stewed tomatoes with bread, maybe that would be a meal. Something like French toast, if we had any eggs. Bread pudding, sometimes with raisins in it. If we got hold of some hamburger, it came to the table more bread than meat. The cookies that were always in the sack with the bread, we just gobbled down straight.

But there were times when there wasn't even a nickel and we would be so hungry we were dizzy. My mother would boil

a big pot of dandelion greens, and we would eat that. I remember that some small-minded neighbor put it out, and
children would tease us, that we ate "fried grass." Sometimes,
if we were lucky, we would have oatmeal or cornmeal mush
three times a day. Or mush in the morning and cornbread
at night.

Philbert and I were grown up enough to quit fighting long
enough to take the .22 caliber rifle that had been our father's,
and shoot rabbits that some white neighbors up or down the
road would buy. I know now that they just did it to help us,
because they, like everyone, shot their own rabbits. Sometimes, I remember, Philbert and I would take little Reginald
along with us. He wasn't very strong, but he was always so
proud to be along. We would trap muskrats out in the little
creek in back of our house. And we would lie quiet until un-
suspecting bullfrogs appeared, and we could spear them, cut
off their legs, and sell them for a nickel a pair to people who
lived up and down the road. The whites seemed less restricted
in their dietary tastes.

Then, about in late 1934, I would guess, something began
to happen. Some kind of psychological deterioration hit our
family circle and began to eat away our pride. Perhaps it was
the constant tangible evidence that we were destitute. We
had known other families who had gone on relief. We had
known without anyone in our home ever expressing it that
we had felt prouder not to be at the depot where the free food
was passed out. And, now, we were among them. At school,
the "on relief" finger suddenly was pointed at us, too, and
sometimes it was said aloud.

It seemed that everything to eat in our house was stamped
Not To Be Sold. All Welfare food bore this stamp to keep
the recipients from selling it. It's a wonder we didn't come
to think of Not To Be Sold as a brand name.

Sometimes, instead of going home from school, I walked
the two miles up the road into Lansing. I began drifting from
store to store, hanging around outside where things like ap-

ples were displayed in boxes and barrels and baskets, and I would watch my chance and steal me a treat. You know what a treat was to me? Anything! . . .

When I began to get caught stealing now and then, the state Welfare people began to focus on me when they came to our house. I can't remember how I first became aware that they were talking of taking me away. What I first remember along that line was my mother raising a storm about being able to bring up her own children. She would whip me for stealing, and I would try to alarm the neighborhood with my yelling. One thing I have always been proud of is that I never raised my hand against my mother. . . .

About this time, my mother began to be visited by some Seventh Day Adventists who had moved into a house not too far down the road from us. They would talk to her for hours at a time, and leave booklets and leaflets and magazines for her to read. She read them, and Wilfred, who had started back to school after we had begun to get the relief food supplies, also read a lot. His head was forever in some book.

Before long, my mother spent much time with the Adventists. It's my belief that what influenced her was that they had even more diet restrictions than she always had taught and practiced with us. Like us, they were against eating rabbit and pork; they followed the Mosaic dietary laws. They ate nothing of the flesh without a split hoof, or that didn't chew a cud. We began to go with my mother to the Adventist meetings that were held further out in the country. For us children, I know that the major attraction was the good food they served. But we listened, too. There were a handful of Negroes, from small towns in the area, but I would say that it was ninety-nine percent white people. The Adventists felt that we were living at the end of time, that the world soon was coming to an end. But they were the friendliest white people I had ever seen. In some ways, though, we children noticed, and, when we were back at home, discussed, that they were different from us—such as the lack of enough seasoning in their food, and the different way that white people smelled.

Meanwhile, the state Welfare people kept after my mother. By now, she didn't make it any secret that she hated them, and didn't want them in her house. But they exerted their right to come, and I have many, many times reflected upon how, talking to us children, they began to plant the seeds of division in our minds. They would ask such things as who was smarter than the other. And they would ask me why I was "so different."

I think they felt that getting children into foster homes was a legitimate part of their function, and the result would be less troublesome, however they went about it.

And when my mother fought them, they went after her—first, through me. I was the first target. I stole; that implied that I wasn't being taken care of by my mother.

All of us were mischievous at some time or another, I more so than any of the rest. Philbert and I kept a battle going. And this was just one of a dozen things that kept building up the pressure on my mother.

I'm not sure just how or when the idea was first dropped by the Welfare workers that our mother was losing her mind.

But I can distinctly remember hearing "crazy" applied to her by them when they learned that the Negro farmer who was in the next house down the road from us had offered to give us some butchered pork—a whole pig, maybe even two of them—and she had refused. We all heard them call my mother "crazy" to her face for refusing good meat. It meant nothing to them even when she explained that we had never eaten pork, that it was against her religion as a Seventh Day Adventist.

They were as vicious as vultures. They had no feelings, understanding, compassion, or respect for my mother. They told us, "She's crazy for refusing food." Right then was when our home, our unity, began to disintegrate. We were having a hard time, and I wasn't helping. But we could have made it, we could have stayed together. As bad as I was, as much trouble and worry as I caused my mother, I loved her.

The state people, we found out, had interviewed the Gohannas family, and the Gohannas' had said that they would take me into their home. My mother threw a fit, though, when she heard that—and the home wreckers took cover for a while.

It was about this time that the large, dark man from Lansing began visiting. I don't remember how or where he and my mother met. It may have been through some mutual friends. I don't remember what the man's profession was. In 1935, in Lansing, Negroes didn't have anything you could call a profession. But the man, big and black, looked something like my father. I can remember his name, but there's no need to mention it. He was a single man, and my mother was a widow only thirty-six years old. The man was independent; naturally she admired that. She was having a hard time disciplining us, and a big man's presence alone would help. And if she had a man to provide, it would send the state people way forever.

We all understood without ever saying much about it. Or at least we had no objection. We took it in stride, even with some amusement among us, that when the man came, our mother would be all dressed up in the best that she had—she still was a good-looking woman—and she would act differently, lighthearted and laughing, as we hadn't seen her act in years.

It went on for about a year, I guess. And then, about 1936, or 1937, the man from Lansing jilted my mother suddenly. He just stopped coming to see her. From what I later understood, he finally backed away from taking on the responsibility of those eight mouths to feed. He was afraid of so many of us. To this day, I can see the trap that Mother was in, saddled with all of us. And I can also understand why he would shun taking on such a tremendous responsibility.

But it was a terrible shock to her. It was the beginning of the end of reality for my mother. When she began to sit around and walk around talking to herself—almost as though she was unaware that we were there—it became increasingly terrifying.

The state people saw her weakening. That was when they began the definite steps to take me away from home. They began to tell me how nice it was going to be at the Gohannas' home, where the Gohannas' and Big Boy and Mrs. Adcock had all said how much they liked me, and would like to have me live with them.

I liked all of them, too. But I didn't want to leave Wilfred. I looked up to and admired my big brother. I didn't want to leave Hilda, who was like my second mother. Or Philbert; even in our fighting, there was a feeling of brotherly union. Or Reginald, especially, who was weak with his hernia condition, and who looked up to me as his big brother who looked out for him, as I looked up to Wilfred. And I had nothing, either, against the babies, Yvonne, Wesley, and Robert.

As my mother talked to herself more and more, she gradually became less responsive to us. And less responsible. The house became less tidy. We began to be more unkempt. And usually, now, Hilda cooked.

We children watched our anchor giving way. It was something terrible that you couldn't get your hands on, yet you couldn't get away from. It was a sensing that something bad was going to happen. We younger ones leaned more and more heavily on the relative strength of Wilfred and Hilda, who were the oldest.

When finally I was sent to the Gohannas' home, at least in a surface way I was glad. I remember that when I left home with the state man, my mother said one thing: "Don't let them feed him any pig.". . .

I would return home to visit fairly often. Sometimes Big Boy and one or another, or both, of the Gohannas' would go with me—sometimes not. I would be glad when some of them did go, because it made the ordeal easier.

Soon the state people were making plans to take over all of my mother's children. She talked to herself nearly all of the time now, and there was a crowd of new white people entering the picture—always asking questions. They would even visit me at the Gohannas'. They would ask me questions out on the porch, or sitting out in their cars.

Eventually my mother suffered a complete breakdown, and the court orders were finally signed. They took her to the State Mental Hospital at Kalamazoo.

It was seventy-some miles from Lansing, about an hour and a half on the bus. A Judge McClellan in Lansing had authority over me and all of my brothers and sisters. We were "state children," court wards; he had the full say-so over us. A white man in charge of a black man's children! Nothing but legal, modern slavery—however kindly intentioned.

My mother remained in the same hospital at Kalamazoo for about twenty-six years. Later, when I was still growing up in Michigan, I would go to visit her every so often. Nothing that I can imagine could have moved me as deeply as seeing her pitiful state. In 1963, we got my mother out of the hospital, and she now lives there in Lansing with Philbert and his family.

It was so much worse than if it had been a physical sickness, for which a cause might be known, medicine given, a cure effected. Every time I visited her, when finally they led her—a case, a number—back inside from where we had been sitting together, I felt worse.

My last visit, when I knew I would never come to see her again—there—was in 1952. I was twenty-seven. My brother Philbert had told me that on his last visit, she had recognized him somewhat. "In spots," he said.

But she didn't recognize me at all.

She stared at me. She didn't know who I was.

Her mind, when I tried to talk, to reach her, was somewhere else. I asked, "Mama, do you know what day it is?"

She said, staring, "All the people have gone."

I can't describe how I felt. The woman who had brought me into the world, and nursed me, and advised me, and chastised me, and loved me, didn't know me. It was as if I was trying to walk up the side of a hill of feathers. I looked at her. I listened to her "talk." But there was nothing I could do.

I truly believe that if ever a state social agency destroyed a family, it destroyed ours. We wanted and tried to stay together. Our home didn't have to be destroyed. But the Welfare, the courts, and their doctor, gave us the one-two-three punch. And ours was not the only case of this kind.

I knew I wouldn't be back to see my mother again because it could make me a very vicious and dangerous person—knowing how they had looked at us as numbers and as a case in their book, not as human beings. And knowing that my mother in there was a statistic that didn't have to be, that existed because of a society's failure, hypocrisy, greed, and lack of mercy and compassion.

4

"When in Rome"

by Mari Evans
(First published 1963)

FROM

American Negro Poetry, edited by Arna Bontemps

In contrast to the overt victimization by white society are the less abusive but consistent slights that black women received as employees in the white world. If not through actual experience, at least through literature, motion pictures, and television, the black woman's role as maid, housekeeper or day worker is familiar to almost everyone. The caricature of a black housekeeper has usually stressed a faithful, good-natured, simplistic and altogether unreal character. However, in the following poem, Mari Evans humorously suggests the limits of the employer's hospitality and reveals that, unlike the stereotype, the black housekeeper is often quite anxious to leave the luxury of her domestic position and return to her own home, impoverished as it might be.

"WHEN IN ROME"

Mattie dear
the box is full
take
whatever you like
to eat . . .
   (an egg
   or soup
   . . . there ain't no meat)

there's endive there
and cottage cheese . . .
    (whew if I had some
    black-eyed peas . . .)
there's sardines
on the shelves
and such . . .
but
don't get my anchovies . . .
they cost
too much!
    (me get the
    anchovies indeed!
    what she think, she got—
    a bird to feed?)
there's plenty in there
to fill you up . . .
    (yes'm. just the
    sight's
    enough!)
(. . . Hope I lives till I get home
I'm tired of eatin'
what they eats
in Rome . . .)

5

FROM

Manchild in the Promised Land

by Claude Brown
(First published 1965)

The legacy of fear resulting from the black woman's oppressive experiences in the white world is illustrated not only by "protective" upbringing of her children, but also by her own fear of the white world. The following selection from Claude Brown's best-selling autobiography describes a young boy's attempt to overcome his mother's fears and assist her in forcing a negligent landlord to respond to their complaints. Throughout, the woman's ingrained apprehension and timidity are displayed.

THIS day that I'd come up to talk was right after a big snowstorm. It was pretty cold; there was a lot of snow in the street. Traffic was moving at a snail's pace, almost at a standstill. Mama was complaining about how cold it was.

"Mama, why don't you complain to the landlord about this?"

"I called the office of the renting agency twice, and they said he wasn't in. When I called the third time, I spoke to him, but he said that it wasn't any of his problem, and I'd have to fix it up myself. I ain't got no money to be gettin' these windows relined."

"Mama, that's a whole lot of stuff. I know better than that. Why don't you go up to the housing commission and complain about it?"

"I ain't got no time to be goin' no place complainin' about nothin'. I got all this housework to do, and all this cookin'; I got to be runnin' after Pimp.* "

"Look, Mama, let's you and me go up there right now. I'm gonna write out a complaint, and I want you to sign it."

"I got all this washin' to do."

"Mama, you go on and you wash. I'm gon wait for you; I'm gon help you wash."

Mama started washing the clothes. As soon as she finished that, she had to put the pot on the stove. Then she had to fix some lunch. As soon as she finished one thing, she would find another thing that she had to do right away. She just kept stalling for time.

Finally, after waiting for about three hours, when she couldn't find anything else to do, I said, "Look, Mama, come on, let's you and me go out there."

We went over to 145th Street. We were going to take the crosstown bus to Broadway, to the temporary housing-commission office.

We were waiting there. Because of the snowstorm, the busses weren't running well, so we waited there for a long time. Mama said, "Look, we'd better wait and go some other time."

I knew she wanted to get out of this, and I knew if I let her go and put it off to another time, it would never be done. I said, "Mama, we can take a cab."

"You got any money?"

"No."

"I ain't got none either. So we better wait until another time."

"Look, Mama, you wait right here on the corner. I'm going across the street to the pawnshop, and when I get back, we'll take a cab."

She waited there on the corner, and I went over to the

* Claude Brown's brother.

pawnshop and pawned my ring. When I came back, we took a cab to Broadway and 145th Street, to the temporary housing-commission office. When I got there, I told one of the girls at the window that I wanted to write out a complaint against a tenement landlord.

She gave me a form to fill out and said I had to make out two copies. I sat down and started writing. It seemed like a whole lot to Mama, because Mama didn't do too much writing. She used a small sheet of paper even when she wrote a letter.

She kept bothering me while I was writing. She said, "Boy, what's all that you puttin' down there? You can't be saying nothin' that ain't the truth. Are you sure you know what you're talking about? Because I'm only complaining about the window, now, and it don't seem like it'd take that much writing to complain about just the one window."

"Mama, you're complaining about all the windows. Aren't all the windows in the same shape?"

"I don't know."

"Well, look here, Mama, isn't it cold in the whole house?"

"Yeah."

"When was the last time the windows were lined?"

"I don't know. Not since we lived in there."

"And you been livin' there seventeen years. Look, Mama, you got to do something."

"Okay, just don't put down anything that ain't true." She kept pulling on my arm.

"Look, Mama, I'm gonna write out this thing. When I finish I'll let you read it, and if there's anything not true in it, I'll cross it out. Okay?"

"Okay, but it just don't seem like it take all that just to write out one complaint."

I had to write with one hand and keep Mama from pulling on me with the other hand. When I finished it, I turned in the two complaint forms, and we left. Mama kept acting so scared, it really got on my nerves. I said, "Look, Mama, you ain't got nothin' to be scared of."

She said she wasn't scared, but she just wanted to stay on the good side of the landlord, because sometimes she got behind in the rent.

"Yeah, Mama, but you can't be freezin' and catching colds just because sometimes you get behind in the rent. Everybody gets behind in the rent, even people who live on Central Park West and Park Avenue. They get behind in the rent. They're not freezin' to death just because they're behind in the rent."

"Boy, I don't know what's wrong with you, but you're always ready to get yourself into something or start some trouble."

"Yeah, Mama, if I'm being mistreated, I figure it's time to start some trouble."

"Boy, I just hope to God that you don't get yourself into something one day that you can't get out of."

"Mama, everybody grows into manhood, and you don't stop to think about that sort of thing once you become a man. You just do it, even if it's trouble that you can't get out of. You don't stop to think. Look, forget about it, Mama. Just let me worry about the whole thing."

"Okay, you do the worryin', but the landlord ain't gon come down there in Greenwich Village and put you out. He gon put us out."

"Mama, he ain't gon put nobody out, don't you believe me?" I pinched her on the cheek, and she got a smile out.

After a couple of days, I came back uptown. I asked Mama, "What about the windows?"

"Nothing about the windows."

"What you mean 'nothin' about the windows'?" I was getting a little annoyed, because she just didn't seem to want to be bothered. I said, "You mean they didn't fix the windows yet? You didn't hear from the landlord?"

"No, I didn't hear from the landlord."

"Well, we're going back up to the housing commission."

"What for?"

"Because we're gon get something done about these windows."

"But something's already been done."

"What's been done, if you didn't hear anything from the landlord?"

"Some man came in here yesterday and asked me what windows."

"What man?"

"I don't know what man."

"Well, what did he say? Didn't he say where he was from?"

"No, he didn't say anything. He just knocked on the door and asked me if I had some windows that needed relining. I said, 'Yeah,' and he asked me what windows, so I showed him the three windows in the front."

"Mama, you didn' show him all the others?"

"No, because that's not so bad, we didn't need them relined."

"Mama, oh, Lord, why didn't you show him the others?"

"Ain't no sense in trying to take advantage of a good thing."

"Yeah, Mama. I guess it was a good thing to you."

I thought about it. I thought about the way Mama would go down to the meat market sometimes, and the man would sell her some meat that was spoiled, some old neck bones or some pig tails. Things that weren't too good even when they weren't spoiled. And sometimes she would say, "Oh, those things aren't too bad." She was scared to take them back, scared to complain until somebody said, "That tastes bad." Then she'd go down there crying and mad at him, wanting to curse the man out. She had all that Southern upbringing in her, that business of being scared of Mr. Charlie. Everybody white she saw was Mr. Charlie.

6

FROM
Children of Crisis
by Robert Coles, M.D.
(First published 1964)

The need for black mothers to protect their children from the dangers of the white world is further explained in the following interview. Here a black woman tells why she thinks it is necessary for her children to "grow up scared of whites" and, more important, why that feeling of apprehension should be buried deep so that her children's hatred is hidden even from themselves.

ONE Negro mother put rather well the feelings I have heard many others express: "I guess we all don't like white people too much deep inside. You could hardly expect us to, after what's happened all these years. It's in our bones to be afraid of them, and bones have a way of staying around even when everything else is gone. But if something is inside of you, it doesn't mean it's there alone. We have to live with one another, black with white I mean. I keep on telling that to the children, and if they don't seem to learn it, like everything else I have to punish them to make sure they do. So I'm not surprised they don't tell me more than you, because they have to obey me; and if I have to obey you and they have to obey me, it's all the same. Just the other day my Laura started getting sassy about white children on the television. My husband told her to hold her tongue and do it fast. It's like with cars and knives, you have to teach your children to know what's dangerous and how to stay away from it, or else they sure won't live long. White people are a real danger to us until we learn how to live with them. So if you want your kids to live long, they have to grow up scared of whites; and the way they get scared is through us; and that's why I don't let my kids get fresh about the white man even in their own house. If I do there's liable to be trouble to pay. They'll forget, and they'll say something outside, and that'll be it for them, and us too. So I make them store it in the bones, way inside, and then no one sees it. Maybe in a joke we'll have once in a while, or something like that, you can see what we feel inside, but mostly it's buried. But to answer your question, I don't think it's only from you it gets buried. The colored man, I think he has to hide what he really feels even from himself. Otherwise there would be too much pain—too much."

7

FROM
Black Rage
by William H. Grier, M.D., and Price M. Cobbs, M.D.
(First published 1968)

*The plight of the black woman in her own community is fi-
nally intricately involved with her historic relationship to
white society, and that relationship has defined and structured
the world within which she has acted and reacted. The next
selection, by black psychiatrists Grier and Cobbs, clarifies the
connection between the divergent experiences in the black
and white world and illuminates the awesome nature of the
black woman's identity crisis.*

IN THE world of women an abundance of feminine narcissism is not only a cheerful attribute but a vital necessity to
emotional well-being. For a woman to invite and accept the
love of a man whom she respects, she must feel herself to be
eminently worthy of his interest and, in a deep and abiding
sense, a lovable person. Such a conviction carries with it a
compelling confidence grown out of the loving engagement
of a mother with her precious child, of a family with a de-
lightful little girl, and of a larger community likewise
charmed by her. With these benevolent auspices, augmented
by real physical attractiveness, the stage is set for the growth
and development of a self-confident woman who can enter
wholeheartedly into love relationships, bringing a richness
and a warmth to her mate and to the children who issue from
their union. The first measure of a child's worth is made by

her mother, and if, as is the case with so many black people in America, that mother feels that she herself is a creature of little worth, this daughter, however valued and desired, represents her scorned self. Thus the girl can be loved and valued only within a limited sphere, and can never be the flawless child, because she is who she is—black and inevitably linked to her black, depreciated mother—always seen to be lacking, deficient, and faulty in some way. Nor can the family or the community at large undo this attitude, since children, however wonderful they may be to adults, are always seen in terms of the future, and in this country the future of a dark girl is dark indeed. While under other circumstances a golden future might be imagined for her, at the very beginning of her life she is comforted and commiserated with and urged to overcome her handicaps—the handicap of being born black.

A certain amount of feminine narcissism must rest ultimately on real physical attractiveness and such attractiveness is determined by the artificial standard each community selects. In this country, the standard is the blond, blue-eyed, white-skinned girl with regular features. Since communication media spread this ideal to every inhabitant of the land via television, newspapers, magazines, and motion pictures, there is not much room for deviation. Women expend great effort in bringing themselves to an approximation of the ideal. The girl who is black has no option in the matter of how much she will change herself. Her blackness is the antithesis of a creamy white skin, her lips are thick, her hair is kinky and short. She is, in fact, the antithesis of American beauty. However beautiful she might be in a different setting with different standards, in this country she is ugly. However loved and prized she may be by her mother, family, and community, she has no real basis of feminine attractiveness on which to build a sound feminine narcissism. When to her physical unattractiveness is added a discouraging, depreciating mother-family-community environment into which she is born, there can be no doubt that she will develop a damaged self-concept and an impairment of her feminine narcissism which will have profound consequences for her character development.

In addition, she takes her place within a historical context, in which women like her have never been valued, have been viewed only as depreciated sexual objects who serve as the recipients of certain debased passions of men who are ashamed to act them out with their own women. Historically she has had some value as a "breeder" of slaves and workmen. But most of all she has been viewed, as all black people have been viewed, as a source of labor; and she has been valued for the amount of work she can perform.

Born thus, depreciated by her own kind, judged grotesque by her society, and valued only as a sexually convenient laboring animal, the black girl has the disheartening prospect of a life in which the cards are stacked against her, and the achievement of a healthy, mature womanhood seems a very long shot indeed. The miracle is that, in spite of such odds, the exceptional love of parents and the exceptional strength of many girls produce so many healthy, capable black women.

One aspect of the black woman's life which attracts little attention from outsiders has to do with her hair. From the time of her birth, the little girl must submit to efforts aimed at changing the appearance of her hair. When she is a babe in arms her hair is brushed and stroked, but in short order the gentle brushing gives way to more vigorous brushing and ultimately combing. Her hair is kinky and combing is painful, but her mother must hold her and force her to submit to it. As far back as her memory will take her, the black woman recalls the painful daily ritual of having her hair combed. It is not insignificant that this painful process is administered in a dispassionate way by the mother. Surely the deadly logic of children would try to explain this phenomenon in some such fashion: "If such pain is administered with such regularity by one who purports to love me, then the end result must be extremely important." And yet, however she might search, the child will never find a reason weighty enough to justify the pain to which she must submit.

For, in fact, the combing and plaiting of the hair, in whatever stylish manner the mother may adopt, results only in the child's being rendered "acceptable." The combing does not produce a stunningly beautiful child from an ugly one, but simply an acceptably groomed child. For the pain she goes through, she might well expect to be stopped on the street by strangers stunned by the beauty and the transformation wrought by the combing and the stylized plaits. Not so. She is simply considered to be of an acceptable appearance.

Again, the logic of children would raise the question: "If Mother has to inflict such pain on me to bring me to the level of acceptability, then I must have been ugly indeed before the combing." For the implications and regularity and torture involved suggest that it is of vital importance that the child not be seen in her "natural state."

Now there is nothing unique about grooming being painful for children. In fact, most people of the soap-and-water cultures may recall the agonies experienced as children when soap got in their eyes. But for most people the discomforts associated with soap, toothbrushes, combs, and slippery bathtubs are transient, experienced mainly by the child who has not quite mastered the technique. It takes only a few years to take most of the pain out of the use of soap and most of the danger out of slippery bathtubs. But for the black girl the combing continues as a daily ritual up to the magic day when she is introduced to the hairdresser.

At the time of this writing the overwhelming majority of Negro women have their hair "fixed" by some method, including the use of a hot comb. The hair is oiled and the heated comb is applied. Usually there is some incidental burning of the scalp. The ordeal itself is long and tiresome, involving hours spent waiting while the overworked beautician moves from customer to customer. To look "presentable" the woman must have her hair pressed every week, or at least every two weeks. Thus the black woman is never free of the painful reminder that she must be transformed from her natural state to some other state in order to appear presentable to her fellow men.

One might ask how this process differs from the ritual to which her Caucasian sister submits for the purpose of similar cosmetic effect. The difference may be a fine one, but it is crucial. The Caucasian woman can brush her hair with a minimum of discomfort and look quite acceptable for any public appearance. If she submits to the pain and discomfort of the hairdresser's, it is for the purpose of *beautification*—it is to enhance her natural appearance which in itself is considered acceptable by her peers. For black women, the pressing comb is like the curse of Eve, a painful, humiliating experience to which she is bound to submit—which, moreover, seems like a wretched legacy grafted into her flesh by her mother.

Almost without exception black women in treatment recall that awful day when they first faced the swimming pool. The black woman's white companions with or without swimming caps plunged into the pool while she stood trembling on the edge, sure that her swimming cap would not fit tightly enough and that afterward she would remove her cap to find disaster.

Women recall the first few weeks at boarding school or college when the issue of having their hair pressed loomed so large. These recollections take on a humorous quality, but the humor is bitter. And not all of it is humor.

A black woman in treatment, who was a borderline schizophrenic, dreaded going to the beauty parlor. She got upset whenever she went and on occasion a visit would be the precipitating incident of her illness. She became delusional and hallucinated. She was terrified in the beauty parlor and thought that the beauticians were whispering behind her back, plotting to do dreadful things to her, and at the very least engaging in malicious gossip. She was terrified of submitting herself to their care. Her associations were to the painful hair combing administered by her devoted grand-

*mother. In her mind the question was never resolved. Did Grand-
mother truly take pleasure in hurting her? This woman's weak
ego may have allowed her to give voice to the silent puzzlement
of her countless healthier sisters.*

As if this were not sufficient, there is one final degradation
associated with hair. Passionate love-making is a vigorous
business and touseled hair is to be expected, but if a woman
perspires too freely, her pressed hair becomes kinky and
must be straightened. And thus even in the triumphant bed
of Eros she is reminded that what should be her crowning
glory is in fact a crown of shame.

It is against this endless cycle of shame, humiliation, and
the implied unacceptability of one's own person that a small
but significant number of black women have turned to the
"natural hairdo"; no hot irons, no pressing combs, no oils,
but a soft, black, gentle cloche of cropped velvet. The effect
is so engaging and feminine, and, in light of the above, so
psychologically redemptive, that we can only wonder why it
has taken them so long, and why even yet there are so few.

Publications designed for Negro audiences have always
found a certain group of advertisers eager to purchase space.
These are the merchants of bleaching creams. The buyers are
promised that the cream will make them "two or three shades
lighter." The advertising space and the prominent display of
these items in neighborhood stores provide objective evidence of what every ghetto dweller knows. Black women have
spent fortunes trying to be white.

Long, straight hair and a fair skin have seemed to be the
requirements for escaping the misery of being a black woman.
One can only guess at the agony of the countless black women
who spent their hard-earned money for a bottled, emulsified
escape from being the way they are. And it is difficult to imagine their frustration and hopelessness when they finally realized that they could not change their hair or their color.

There surely is nothing more cruelly contained than the

feminine narcissism in American black women. To para-
phrase Countee Cullen:

> *And yet I wonder at this thing*
> *To make a woman black and bid her sing.*

There have been lesser sources of misery too, as if these
were not enough. Black women felt ashamed if their feet were
big. They hid their feet and bought shoes that were too small
and often earned a lifetime of foot problems.

Most cultures associate big feet with lower-class origins and
thus the women (and men) value small feet. For the American Negro, "lower class" does not adequately state the condition he wants to rise above. For him, "lower class" has over-
tones of slavery and the lash, and the black woman's shame
when her feet are large is therefore a deeper wound and a
more lasting hurt.

They have also felt a special misery over skinny legs and
small breasts. In fact, there was a heightened concern over all
the criteria of femininity—all the criteria of physical beauty
thrust upon them by a society which held beauty to be the
opposite of what they were.

The softly seductive, essentially feminine quality of women
is at its height during adolescence. In this country great efforts are expended in extending the period, both backward
and forward. Backward, to the preadolescence of eleven- and
twelve-year-olds, and forward, past the sixties and seventies
to the end of a woman's life. Whatever the chronological
boundaries, the effort clearly is to extend them and make it
possible for a woman to appear more feminine for a longer
period of her life.

For a great many black women, however, the process is reversed. Black women seem unconsciously to shorten this period more drastically than their poor circumstances might
necessitate. In their thirties and forties they seem to give up
competition for male interest. They neglect their figures, allow themselves to become obese, concern themselves more

with the utility of their clothing and less with style, and resign themselves to a relatively asexual maternal role in which work and a hovering concern for the family occupies them entirely. They give the impression that they have no interest in men in a sexual way. The total effect such women give can be startling.

A group of relatively poor black mothers who were seen in therapy appeared at first glance to be in their forties or fifties. They were, however, all in their late twenties. Their shapeless garments, unattractive shoes, dental neglect, and general disinterest in their appearance made them seem twenty to thirty years older than they actually were.

A similar disinterest in physical appearance may be noticed in their white counterparts, but the careful observer will see a sharper, chronologically earlier, and a much more widespread relinquishment of youth on the part of black women.

The abandonment of youthful narcissism and the associated competition for male attention can occur at even earlier ages, and in fact may begin at such an early age as to subvert even the high-spirited period of adolescence.

Those who deal with the problems of adolescence are concerned about the high frequency of obesity in Negro girls. The authors are well aware that obesity is a problem of adolescence for young girls of every ethnic origin in the United States. But statistics seem to show that obesity is very much more frequent among black girls. It is also well known that women and mothers who find themselves heavily burdened with problems of day-to-day management and survival find it difficult to expend much energy on feminine frills and finery. But the incidence of abandonment of feminine adornment and narcissistic interest is much greater among black women and is not a direct function of their poverty or disadvantaged circumstances. In fact, however slow has been the movement of black people as a group toward greater advantages, a small rise in income lifts the burden of black women to a very significant degree.

Only a short time ago her task as a home maker was prodigious; home appliances are relatively recent luxuries. One would think, therefore, that she would now have more time and more energy to devote to her own person and to the pleasures of femininity. But the whole issue of work and responsibility has no place in any attempt to explain the obesity and the associated abandonment of sexual competition by adolescent black girls.

If this surrender cuts across all age groups, one must look for other reasons. The most satisfactory explanation would be that femininity is only imperfectly grasped by most black women in any event, since femininity in this society is defined in such terms that it is out of reach for her. If the society says that to be attractive is to be white, she finds herself unwittingly striving to be something she cannot possibly be; and if femininity is rooted in feeling oneself eminently lovable, then a society which views her as unattractive and repellent has also denied her this fundamental wellspring of femininity.

So it may be that after a brief struggle a black woman feels that femininity, as it is defined in these times, is something she cannot achieve. Rather than having her heart broken every day, she relinquishes the struggle and diverts her interest elsewhere. She has derived none of the intensely personal satisfaction she might have received as an honored and desirable sexual object.

There is another factor in her ready rejection of youth, and it has deep historical roots. It has been said that beauty is a curse to a subject woman. From the time black people arrived in this country up to the very recent years black women have been sexually available to any white man who felt so inclined. They were not protected by the laws and their men stood in jeopardy of life if a hand was raised in their defense. For the slave or subject woman, youth and beauty meant arousing the interest of the oppressor and exposure to sexual exploitation.

The black girl found herself in a peculiar vise. If her

dreams were realized and she grew into a beauty, her problems were far from solved and had in fact only begun. She
now attracted the attention of the oppressor, who turned her
femininity to the service of his own sexual appetite.

Thus youth and beauty, though desired, were also dreaded
as the certain bearer of trouble and strife.

Even now, the pressures on the pretty girl of the ghetto are
great and it requires a special heroism for her to avoid the
identity of an anonymous sexual object.

Small wonder that black women flee the beauty of youth.

Much of our discussion has dealt with feminine narcissism
from a genetic, dynamic, and adaptive point of view. But the
perception of oneself in a favorable light includes the identification of oneself in a historical, sequential sense as well.
Group identity and the gathering to oneself of the joys and
sufferings of one's forebears play an important part in the con-
struction of a self-identity. The United States presents to all
its citizens, but most vividly to the black woman, a negative
as well as a positive ideal. The positive ideal, as mentioned
above, is in many ways unobtainable for her, inasmuch as it
really involves trying to become less Negro and more white.
She must be clean, neat, modest, subdued, with hair straightened and hopefully with skin lightened. The negative ideal
or paradigm is the black, slovenly, obese, dirty, promiscuous
woman. But of all the words, perhaps the most important are
those that designate the black woman as ugly and repellent.
Of the two forces moving her, the pull and attraction of the
positive ideal and the push and repulsion of the negative, the
latter is by far the more powerful.

Her situation is made worse by the fact that she can by no
means approximate the positive ideal and feels always in danger of finding herself too close to the negative. Moreover, the
central position of feminine narcissism in the development of
character presents a problem for the black woman in her
evaluation of her intelligence. Intellectual achievement is
closely linked to healthy narcissism. With an impairment of

narcissism, a sound synthesis of intellectual accomplishment within the character structure is difficult to achieve.

The full flowering of a woman's sexual function and her capacity to enjoy it are based on her evaluation of herself. If she considers herself an especially worthwhile person, she can joyfully submit to her lover, knowing that he will likewise prize and value her. Her enjoyment of the sexual function will not be impaired by the feeling of being degraded by the man. There is, however, a more subtle interaction between narcissism and the sexual function in women. There is a natural inclination for a woman to yield herself to a powerful lover, gaining additional narcissistic supplies in her possession of him. Her own high evaluation of herself, in turn, evokes in the man a similar high evaluation of her. If her narcissism is impaired, the sexual act is a degrading submission to a man who does not value her, and she arises from it feeling a loss of self-esteem rather than a personal enhancement.

The Negro woman's black face, African features, and kinky hair are physical attributes which place her far from the American ideal of beauty, and make her, with reference to the American ideal, ugly. When the feeling of ugliness is reinforced by the rejection of family and society, the growing girl develops a feeling not only of being undesirable and unwanted but also of being mutilated—of having been fashioned by Nature in an ill-favored manner. Anatomy determines that every little girl will struggle with feelings of having been injured and mutilated when she compares her sexual organs with the male's, but under normal circumstances the compensatory blossoming of narcissism allows her to develop a feeling of satisfaction with herself. The black woman's feelings of mutilation, both psychical and physical, are strengthened by her experiences and she is guarded from self-depreciation only by an enfeebled narcissism. As a result, her personal ambitions as an adolescent and her capacity to live out her aspirations suffer. Under the sign of discouragement and rejection which governs so much of her physical operation, she is inclined to organize her personal ambitions in terms of her achievements and to find these achievements serving to compensate for other losses and hurts.

A dark woman who had risen rapidly in her profession experienced a worsening of her chronic depression. As her achievements grew she found opportunistic men taking an interest in her. She developed intense feelings of bitterness about her job, which she felt was the only element in her attractiveness to men. She was bitter about her intellect which had brought her to her present position. She now was attractive to men who were shallow, opportunistic fortune seekers. To compound her misery, she felt an inclination to accept even these shallow men for whatever they wanted in her.

In choosing a mate, the black woman is again faced with the undesirability of her blackness and with the fact that it is the rare black man who can resist the omnipresent presentation of the white ideal. The compromises that are necessary in the establishment of any relationship between a man and a woman can easily be felt by her to be profound compromises with her own aspirations for a love relationship. She may feel that the compromises are based, not on the difficulties faced by two quite different individuals in adjusting to an intimate union, but on the fact that her "unattractiveness" makes it impossible for her to obtain the "ideal" man.

Thus, the contemporary implications of her Negro-ness and the historical identity it imposes on her make her progress to healthy womanhood much more difficult. The problems we have spelled out here represent barriers which are high but not insurmountable. Because we also see evidence of the remarkable capacity of black people in America to survive, we see one of the adaptive modes chosen by black women to make their way in a hostile world. With youthful narcissism crushed and sexual life perverted, they drew back from these modes as primary means of life expression. Letting youth go, beauty go, and sex go, they narrowed their vision to the most essential feminine function—mothering, nurturing, and protecting their children. In such a role the black woman has been the salvation of many a family. To call such a family matriarchal, as many have done, is to obscure the essential maternal function and to suggest authority for authority's sake.

We suggest that the black woman has been beset by cruelty on all sides and as a result centered her concern on the most essential quality of womanhood. In so doing she stood by her mate or in his stead when he was crippled or crushed by the oppressor.

The mother in the play *Raisin in the Sun*—who stands as a bulwark of reason between her family and an irrational world —reflects the perception by black women of that essential female function of mothering and its triumph in a world which robs her of other joys.

So much of black women's suffering has grown out of the same feeling of helplessness that has pilloried the male. With the new black movements under way, all that we have just said may assume merely historical significance. The contorted efforts to be white, the shame of the black body, the rejection of youth—may all vanish quickly. Negro women need only see that, truly, "black is beautiful."

8

"I Just Want to Be Myself"

by Lena Horne
(First published 1963)

FROM
Show Magazine

*Few Afro-Americans have had as much contact or involve-
ment with white society as successful black entertainers. Until
very recently, they so dominated white America's conception
of black people that they were often elevated to the position
of "spokesmen" for all blacks. The disproportionate attention given to black performers and the responsibility that
accompanied their role made their lives especially difficult.
For the black woman the situation was perhaps more griev-
ous. Though financially successful and perhaps tops in her
field, she could not escape America's refracted view of blacks.
She still had to face the stereotyped conceptions of the "respectable servant" or the "whore." Constantly in the spot-
light, she was a readily accessible mark for the exploitative
forces in American society.*

*Lena Horne, one of the first black entertainers to escape
the "chitlin' circuit" and work with top billing in white es-
tablishments, describes in the following selection her rise to
fame and her introduction to the white entertainment world.
Her description of financial and political exploitation, of
white men on the prowl for black flesh, and of the discrim-
inatory practices of night club owners who employed black*

entertainers, but refused black customers, are still represen-
tative, even though the events of the past decade have lessened
their intensity. The difficulty of the black woman's search for
identity within the context of the white world is also indi-
cated by Miss Horne's description of her marriages—to both
black and white men—and her final commitment to the civil
rights movement.

PERHAPS the beginning of the story is October 1919 and a
picture in an N.A.A.C.P. magazine called *The Branch Bul-*
letin. There is a trim, chubby child in a white dress and bon-
net holding a disinterested rose and wearing high-topped
shoes. The caption reads:

> *This is a picture of one of the youngest members of the*
> *N.A.A.C.P. Her name is Lena Calhoun Horne and she lives in*
> *Brooklyn, N. Y. She paid the office a visit last month and seemed*
> *delighted with everything she saw, particularly the National Sec-*
> *retary and the telephones.*

I came from what was called one of the First Families of
Brooklyn. It was a family that never talked about the fact that
we are all the descendants of slave women. Yet it was the rape
of slave women by their masters which accounted for our
white blood, which, in turn, made us Negro "society." I realize now, that as a child and young girl, I did not know who
I was or what I was—because nobody ever told me. My grandmother was an ardent fighter for equality and member of the
N.A.A.C.P., but even she, the direct issue of a slave owner,
never really understood why she was fighting. To her it was
simply an unconscious and unmentionable fact of life that it
was tough to be a Negro woman. I certainly never learned
anything about my identity in school, because the only Negro
mentioned in history books was George Washington Carver,
and he was too pure and good to believe, though I did learn
that other races had backgrounds they looked upon with
pride. I kept trying to find some reason to feel the same way.

Eventually, when "interested" people began to try and give me different "images" of myself, I came to the realization that nobody (and certainly not yet myself) seemed to understand the Negro woman who stood between the two conventionally accepted extremes: the "good," *quiet* colored woman who scrubbed and cooked and maybe made a respectable servant, and the whore. . . .

So, by the time I was 16 and had returned to Brooklyn after spending seven years in the South, I may not have known who I was, but I had a pretty good idea of what white people were, and what they thought *we* were. My grandmother was dead, my parents were divorced and my mother and I had to eat, so I left the polite world of the Brooklyn branch of the N.A.A.C.P. and became a chorine at the Cotton Club. I worked for white hoods who hired the greatest Negro talent of the day but wouldn't let Negro people into the club, though it was smack in the middle of Harlem. If the little contact that I had with white people in the South had left me with small fondness for them, the Cotton Club made it easy for me to hate them. In the South I had been too young to see the Negro woman used as anything else but a servant. But at the Cotton Club, my mother sat protectively in my dressing room every night because there was not the slightest doubt as to what the white hoods and the white "swells" in New York wanted to do with Negro women. Thank God, as Duke Ellington used to say, I was jailbait. Even as a performer I sensed that the white people in the audience saw nothing but my flesh, and its color, onstage. I was not ready for this. I had never lived outside the Negro ghetto. I didn't know anything about white people. I often sensed that some members of my family disliked them, but I didn't know why. All I knew was that I was not supposed to like them either. Considering conditions at the Cotton Club, that was easy. If I had to have a word with one of the bosses I said "Good Evening, Mr. Whomever" or "How do you do, Mr. Whatsyourname," but I never *spoke* to them.

I came to realize that part of my family's dislike was based simply on fear. My mother was afraid of the owners, my stepfather was afraid of them and I suppose I was, too. To me, they were always "those people." In the end, my mother virtually had to kidnap me to get me away from them. They had signed me to what amounted to a lifetime contract. They could have gone on exploiting me for years. That was my introduction to the white world.

A very respected Negro orchestra leader named Noble Sissle helped my mother get me out of the Cotton Club, and I toured with him for a year. Noble helped me learn a little singing and gave me the kind of fatherly advice I had come to expect from my family and other respectable Negro people. "Remember, you are a lady, you are not a whore—don't let them treat you like one." This is easy to say, but it is almost irrelevant when you're on tour and can't find a place to eat or sleep after you've played and sung for white dances. One night in Indiana there was, as usual, nowhere to stay. A circus was wintering there and a white man—I guess you could call him a "white liberal"—let us sleep at circus headquarters. The animals howled all night long. By that time I didn't care if they treated me like a lady and I didn't care if they treated me like a whore—I just wanted to be treated like a human being. I had not learned to be tough, so the only escape that I saw was to run away from it all and get married.

I married a man who was the recipient of all the stress, of all the cruel meaning of being a Negro man in America at that time and in that generation. He had been to college—a Southern Negro college—and he was terribly proud. But he was often refused work because of the color of his skin. When he finally got a job it was a reward for the work he and his brothers had done with the young Democrats in Pittsburgh (which is where we lived). They gave him a job as a clerk in the county coroner's office. God knows it was tough for everybody in the Thirties—but he was a capable and sensitive man, and it galled him to see white men with less ability getting the jobs he felt he could do. And I was no help to him at all.

Look at what I was: I had left school at 16 to be a chorine in a joint and a singer in a touring band. I had married to get *away* from that, not to *bring* anything to my husband. So after a day of frustration, contending with the white man's world, my husband would come home to find a young, dumb wife who had had two children quickly, but who didn't even know how to cook or sew or keep house. I certainly was not his idea of a good wife and mother.

—I think Negro wives, no matter what their age or background or even their understanding of the problem, have to be terribly strong—much stronger than their white counterparts. They cannot relax, they cannot simply be loving wives waiting for the man of the house to come home. They have to be spiritual sponges, absorbing the racially inflicted hurts of their men. Yet at the same time they have to give him courage, to make him know that it is worth it to go on, to go back day after day to the humiliations and discouragement of trying to make it in the white man's world for the sake of their families. It's hard enough for a poor working white man, but a hundred times harder for a Negro. —

It isn't easy to be both a sponge and an inspiration—often it doesn't leave enough room for simple love. And you both become victims of the system you are trying to fight. So I was an exploited Negro woman who was not brave enough or smart enough to make my marriage work. And he was a Negro man who, whether he admitted it or not, found me lacking. We were divorced.

With the breakup of my marriage I had to go back to my so-called career. During the Pittsburgh years, to help earn money, I had been singing around town for white people at their parties. So I knew I could still go back to the only real thing I had learned how to do. Maybe I didn't know how to be a wife, but I knew how to sing.

In 1940, I auditioned for Charlie Barnet and joined his band. This meant not only going back to a career but also

going back to the hated white world. I must say that Charlie
and the boys (who were white) were wonderful to me and,
corny as it sounds, taught me that some white people (at least
the musicians) could be trusted. If some restaurants wouldn't
serve me or some hotel wouldn't give me a room, the whole
band would just get up and walk out. And later, Barney Jo-
sephson, the owner of Cafe Society Downtown on Sheridan
Square, gave me a job, but only after giving me hell for
using "Sleepy Time Down South" as an audition song. It is
a little ironic that the first people to teach me any sort of professional self-respect were white. Unfortunately the rest of
the white world was rarely so understanding.

At this point I discovered a different kind of "image" that
white people have of Negroes. There were some nightclub
owners who wouldn't hire me because I didn't look and
sound "colored enough"—whatever that means. It was the
same when I went to Hollywood. As a matter of fact, Max
Factor discovered light Egyptian pancake makeup while trying to concoct something that would make me look the way
they felt a Negro woman should look in front of the camera.
(The upshot of *that* was that a lot of white actresses started
getting work playing Egyptians and mulattoes—roles that
could have gone to Negroes.) And, naturally, M-G-M always
shot my scenes so that they could be cut out when the picture
played in the South. Some people even suggested that I develop a Spanish accent so that I could be passed off as a Latin
type. All this time, Walter White of the N.A.A.C.P. was writing letters saying "remember your position" (in other words,
don't disgrace us). It was not easy to be a "pioneer" in Hollywood.

I was learning that life outside the ghetto is sometimes
more difficult than life inside it. In order not to break, especially as a woman, you have to develop a certain guile and
toughness. It is the only means of not letting *them* get to you
—of not letting *them* see that they can hurt you. I might have
chosen to let my protective covering be more "colored"—I

could have sung spirituals and blues; or I might have gone the other way—and developed the Spanish accent. But by this time I had a lot more ego, maybe not the right kind, but enough to make damn sure that nobody but *me* was going to pick my "image."

I developed an isolation from the audience that was actually only a sophisticated cover for hostility. But the audience didn't see it; they were too busy seeing their own preconceived images of a Negro woman. The image that I myself chose to give them was of a woman whom they could not reach. I think this is why I rarely speak to an audience. I am too proud to let *them* think they can have any personal contact with me. They get the singer, but they are not going to get the woman. I think many Negro performers feel much the same way and they find their own methods of letting people know it. In other words we all find our own means of rebellion.

In the Forties, therefore, I had become both a success and a rebel. At one point the studio wanted me to do a Broadway show in which they had money, *St. Louis Woman,* but I refused. Why should I do a show for them when they wouldn't give me a real part in a picture? They "punished" me by making me tour practically every Loew's vaudeville house in the country.

At this same time, I discovered that I could be exploited by yet another kind of white man. This time it was the politician who used me to project yet another kind of "image"— a political one. I spoke at rallies and meetings, and even though I believed in their causes, I knew that they had no care for me or contact with me as an individual. I was just being exploited for another use.

The only people with whom I felt I could still be myself were musicians, white or Negro. They didn't seem to care about me as anything but a singer and a human being. After the six-to-six grind at M-G-M I would go to wherever Nat Cole or Wynonie Harris was working and listen to them.

They and others that I had known in New York were people with whom I could be really comfortable.

It was at this point that I met the man who was to become my husband, Lennie Hayton. He happens to be white, and he also happens to be a musician. He was a composer and arranger at the studio when we met. I think, given my experience, that I could not have married anyone but a musician, since they were the only people with whom I felt I could be myself.

Obviously, a lot of people, both white and Negro, didn't like this marriage. In fact, most of *my* family stopped speaking to me. But Lennie's own mother and sister were absolutely wonderful. Lennie grew up in a closely knit Jewish family from New York which respected artists and musicians and had no racial prejudice.

What all of the critics of my marriage failed to realize was that Lennie came into my life at a time when I was beginning to feel the pressure of the self-imposed isolation of my career as well as the self-imposed discipline of being a mother. This kind of situation is very difficult for *any* woman who is alone. With Lennie, I could try to be a good wife—and he was naturally able to give *me* the kind of support that I needed from a husband. Lennie had not had to grow up under the same kind of pressure that the average Negro man has to take. When we married he was an accomplished musician who had already achieved status as a professional. He could understand my drives and ambitions, as well as my inadequacies, without blaming me for not being able to help *him*. He helped me professionally and he helped me emotionally—because he didn't have an ax to grind with the world. He is a much kinder and much more loving person than I am. I still hate and am suspicious of too many people, both white and Negro. But I have tried to learn from his humanity, and I'm still learning. And it is because of my marriage to Lennie that I am able to channel and direct most of my frustrations about the race question, instead of exploding in impotent rage.

I have been asked by people who obviously don't know me very well how I feel when I look at television and see white policemen knocking down Negro women with fire hoses and then look at my husband and know that he is white. This kind of question is just as stupid and unfortunately just as normal as the people who make it. Don't they understand that when you look at people you love—husband or friend— you don't see *color?* It so happens that Lennie is the kindest person I have ever known. And I know that his reaction to savagery is just as strong, if not stronger than my own. I say that his reaction might be stronger because he is perhaps less used to it than I am.

Despite my involvement in my own problems and despite the contentment I have found in marriage, I find that it is impossible for me to ignore the larger Negro struggle. Maybe it is because I am automatically an angry person, or maybe it's only because my grandmother made me a member of the N.A.A.C.P. when I was two years old, but basically I think it is because no Negro, whatever his situation in life, is able to ignore it. Anyway, the struggle is becoming a revolution and I want to be a part of it in whatever role I can fill best. I have only one condition in terms of my joining the fight— I intend always to speak for *myself.* I am not a "spokesman" for the Negro people nor am I a spokesman for any particular organizational branch of the fight.

Naturally, any decision to join a revolutionary movement involves a certain kind of commitment. And naturally this kind of commitment cannot be made blindly. I am grateful that I had Lennie to help me make the decision. When Jim Baldwin called me in California and asked me to come to that now "famous" (or "infamous") meeting with Robert Kennedy, the Attorney General, I was torn, for many reasons. First of all, I hate flying. Secondly, although I have my own opinions about the question, I was not sure what I could contribute in a meeting of that sort (although I had always felt that the Attorney General was someone whom we could approach). Last, and most important, I knew that my commitment could not stop there. When Lennie and I discussed my going, he settled the question very simply by saying, "Go ahead. If you don't go, maybe you won't love *me* anymore."

9

"The Scarlet Woman"

by Fenton Johnson
(First published around 1916)

FROM

Poetry of the Negro
edited by Langston Hughes and Arna Bontemps

*Having been made the repository of America's sexual myths
and usually faced with the prospect of abject poverty, the
sporting life and prostitution were constant temptations for
black women. In the following poem, Fenton Johnson (1888–
1958) describes a black woman who, having her estimation of
her personal worth eroded by a racist society, is led into a life
of vice and the search for alcoholic oblivion. In her initial
predicament and her ultimate resolution, her experiences
symbolize the social dilemma confronting many black women.*

THE SCARLET WOMAN

Once I was good like the Virgin Mary and the Minister's wife.
My father worked for Mr. Pullman and white people's tips; but
   he died two days after his insurance expired.
I had nothing, so I had to go to work.
All the stock I had was a white girl's education and a face that
   enchanted the men of both races.
Starvation danced with me.

So when Big Lizzie, who kept a house for white men, came to me
    with tales of fortune that I could reap from the sale of my
    virtue I bowed my head to Vice.
Now I can drink more gin than any man for miles around.
Gin is better than all the water in Lethe.

10

FROM

Lady Sings the Blues

by Billie Holiday
(First published 1956)

*Billie Holiday grew up in Baltimore in an impoverished,
broken home. These experiences naturally compounded her
difficulties in confronting the hostility of the white world.
This excerpt from her autobiography begins when she was
thirteen years old. The events described here are not unique
among blacks who have been raised under similar circumstances, except that Billie Holiday possessed a vocal genius
that would temporarily liberate her. Still, driven to drugs by
her experiences, she died in 1959 at the age of forty-four.*

EVERYBODY was talking about Lindbergh's hop to Paris
that summer of 1927 when I made it solo from Baltimore to
New York.

From the day she got me sprung from the Catholic institution, Mom and I were drug with Baltimore. We had had it
with roomers after the deal with Mr. Dick. There was nothing to do except for Mom to go back slaving away as somebody's maid. In Baltimore she couldn't make half the loot she
could up North. So I dragged my scrub brush and bucket
from house to house trying to make up the difference that
could keep us together.

One night I came home long after dark. I had worked all
day and had ninety cents to show for it. Mom took one look
at me and busted out crying. I looked that beat. I tried to

comfort her and tell her I'd be all right, but she kept saying, "There's got to be something better than this." And if there was, she and I knew it had to be up North. It wasn't going to be in Baltimore.

So up she went. And back I went into the little house with Cousin Ida and her husband, Grandma and Grandpop, little Cousin Henry and Elsie—to wait for the day Mom could send for me to come to New York.

Life with Cousin Ida was just more of the same. I couldn't wait for it to be over, and then I hated the way it ended. She was one of the worst black bitches God ever put on earth, but I hated the way she died. Goiters ran in my mother's family; Mom had one, but Cousin Ida's was the worst, a great big horrible one that hung from her chin to her breast. One day she had a choking spell and there was nobody around to help her but her husband, and he was passed out drunk. She died like a dog, on her knees, choking for air. The doctor said if her man had even come to enough to raise the window and let in some air he could have saved her. But he was too juiced even for that. Mean as she was, I hated to see her die like that.

In those days they kept dead bodies around for two weeks for the waking and crying. Cousin Ida and her husband were Baptists and they gave Mom and me a hard time because we were Catholic. We were always accused of thinking we were better than the Baptists. They used to make fun of Mom with her candles and creeping up to the altar. So when I refused to look at Cousin Ida's body they thought it had something to do with that. They wouldn't let me alone. Finally, when I wouldn't go near the coffin, someone dragged me over by it, held me up, and made me look at her. I was sick from that.

With Cousin Ida dead and nobody to look after Henry and Elsie, let alone me, Mom sent for me to come to New York. I finished up the fifth grade, and as soon as school was out Grandpop put one of those big tags around my neck, saying who I was and where I was going. Grandma made me this big basket of fried chicken, hard-boiled eggs—enough food to last

Lindbergh across the Atlantic. And Grandpop put me on the train. I had a ticket to Long Branch, where Mom was going to meet me. But as soon as I got on the train by myself I decided, damn Long Branch, I was going to get to see Harlem someway. So I took off the big tag, decided I'd get off the train in New York, take the subway to Harlem, have myself a time, and then contact my mother.

I was only thirteen, but I was a hip kitty. I was travelling light—except for that basket of chicken—but I was travelling. When I got off at Pennsylvania Station in New York, I had never seen a place so big. I was wandering around, taking my own sweet time, looking at all the big buildings, taking it all in. I must have been a sight, traipsing around, gawking, with this basket of chicken and my little suitcase. Anyway, this social worker spotted me and she knew damn well I was lost.

It was dark by then. This social worker was white, but she was nice as she could be. She asked me where I had come from, what my name was, where I was going, who my mother was, and all that stuff. But I wouldn't tell her anything, not even my name. Nobody was going to stop me from getting to Harlem. It turned out this woman was with the Society for the Prevention of Cruelty to Children. She was going to put me in the shelter they had, but it was too late already, the place was closed for the night. This turned out to be a break.

She took me and bought me dinner and then we went to a beautiful hotel where she got me a fine room with a bed all to myself. This place knocked me out. Years later I went back there to see the place and found it was only a YWCA—but it looked like the Waldorf Astoria then. This woman was so nice I tried to get her to give me a job.

"I'll work for you hard," I told her. "I'll clean your house, wash your steps, scrub your floors." But then she'd ask me my name and I still wouldn't tell her. She was wise to me. She'd smile when I refused to tell her my name. "I know you know," she'd tell me. "You're smart."

The next morning she came and took me to the home run

by the Society. It was nice there. The food was good. There
were plenty of kids around and nothing to do but play. There
was a huge playground out back, with slides and swings and
things, screened at the sides and the top.

I must have stayed there a couple of weeks before Mom
found out where they had me. They took me downstairs one
morning to meet the lady who had come to pick me up. It
wasn't my mother, though. It was a woman by name of Mrs.
Levy.

"I'm not going with you," I told her right off. "I'm staying."

"Why?" she asked me. "What's the matter?"

"Nothing," I told her, "I like this place."

"But I came to take you to your mama," she told me.

I noticed she didn't say "mother" and she didn't say
"mammy." She said "mama." And the way she said it kind of
made me think I might take a chance. Mrs. Levy was the lady
from Long Branch Mom worked for. Mom was taking care
of her kids, she told me, and she had drove down in her car to
take me home with her.

When I heard she had a car, that settled it. And when I
saw the pretty automobile, I was ready to go anywhere just
for the ride. I hadn't been in a car so many times that I could
take a chance missing a ride. We drove from downtown New
York to Long Branch.

Sadie and I were going to be together again at last. We were
going to make it. She even had a job lined up for me—as a
maid, naturally. What else?

The woman I was to work for was big, fat and lazy. She
didn't do a thing all day except lay her big ass on the beach.
I didn't do much more. All I had to do was sleep and eat, peel
a few onions and vegetables to keep her hands pretty, wash a
few dishes to keep them from getting rough, and dust a little
so she wouldn't have to move around.

This great big greasy bitch didn't do a thing all day until
about fifteen minutes before her old man was due home for

dinner. Then she would kick up a storm. I didn't know my way around her fancy kind of joint. Instead of telling me what she wanted me to do, she'd get excited because her husband was waiting, start hollering at me and calling me "nigger." I had never heard that word before. I didn't know what it meant. But I could guess from the sound of her voice. It was weird, that house—filled with crazy furniture and junk that just collected dust—and pillows all over. How she used to dog me about those pillows!

It didn't last long. One day, just before she hauled off to the beach, she dragged out a big old blanket, threw it at me, and told me to wash it. I flipped. I wasn't supposed to do laundry, so I told her what she could do with her damn blanket. That was the end of that job. In the first place, I didn't want to be her maid, or anybody's. I figured there had to be something better than this.

When I went back to Mom's and told her what happened, she didn't know what the hell to do with me. She knew I'd never make it as a maid. I had finished the fifth grade in school in Baltimore and I hadn't been back. If I did go back, they might ask where the hell I had been. There was no place for me to go to school anyway, unless I had a place to live. Mom had a little money saved, and she finally said she'd take me to Harlem and board me out.

Mom wasn't really a square at all. Yet in many ways she was. The place she found for me to live was nothing less than a fancy apartment house off 141st Street in Harlem. People paid some high old rent there then. Mom got me a room in a beautiful apartment belonging to a lady named Florence Williams. I hadn't emptied basins, laid out Lifebuoy soap and towels in Alice Dean's place in Baltimore for nothing. I knew what was cooking. But Mom didn't. She paid my rent in advance to Florence, and with the straightest face in the world asked this handsome sharply dressed madam to take care of her little girl. Florence was one of the biggest madams in Harlem.

She might just as well have asked little Eleanora [Billie Holiday's given name] to take care of Florence. I thought I was a real hip kitty. In a matter of days I had my chance to become a strictly twenty-dollar call girl—and I took it. The Jelke stuff they made a big deal out of wasn't even new then. The only thing new about it—even to me—was the fancy telephone. I had seen those funny-looking telephones in the movies—the ones you answer lying in bed instead of the old-time wall jobs. From the moment I saw them I knew that was for me. Not just any kind, though. It had to be a white telephone. And that's what I had at Florence's place.

I soon had two young white cats to match I could depend on regular every week, one on Wednesday, one Saturday. Sometimes one of them would make it twice a week. The madam took five out of every twenty dollars for the rent. This still left me more than I could make in a damn month as a maid. And I had someone doing *my* laundry. It was a small place. Florence only had two other girls, a yellow one named Gladys and a white girl whose name I don't remember.

It wasn't long before I had money to buy a few things I'd always wanted—my first honest-to-God silk dress and a pair of spike-heeled ten-dollar patent-leather pumps.

But I didn't have what it took to be a call girl. In the first place, and for damn good reason, I was scared to death of sex. First there had been the deal with Mr. Dick. Then when I was twelve a trumpet player from a big Negro orchestra had had me for the first time on the floor of my grandmother's parlour. That was rugged enough to finish me with men for a while. I remember being hurt so, I thought I was going to die. I went to Mom, took my bloody clothes and threw them down in disgust.

"So this is what you and Pop used to do when I slept at the foot of your bed in a cedar chest," I screamed at her.

What could she say? Nothing. She moaned a little about her baby having had a man and she worried herself half to death for days for fear I would have a baby the way she had

had me. I had hit her where she couldn't hit back. I swore then I was through with men and I told her she needn't worry any more about me doing what she and Pop had done.

Then one day at Florence's place a big Negro had come in and insisted on having nobody but me. He gave me fifty dollars. He should have. It was a small price to pay for nearly killing me. I was out of commission for days and couldn't even put my two feet on the floor. Mom came to see me during that time and found me sick in bed. She didn't know what had been going on, but after one look at me she said she was taking me to the hospital.

I was so sick I didn't care if I went—until I saw the letters on the cap of the cat who came with the ambulance cart. I had heard about that hospital he came from. Girls I knew went there with pneumonia and came out without any ovaries. So I sat right up in bed, sent the ambulance away, crawled to the bathroom, had something to eat later, and I was all right.

No wonder I was scared to death of sex. And no wonder I did what I did when a Negro cat came around by the name of Big Blue Rainier. He was with Bub Hewlett, who was running Harlem in those days. Both of them are dead now, but they were big men then.

I went to jail for refusing to go to bed with Blue. I tried to tell him it wasn't anything personal, I just wasn't going to bed with any more Negroes.

With my regular white customers, it was a cinch. They had wives and kids to go home to. When they came to see me it was wham, bang, they gave me the money and were gone. I made all the loot I needed. But Negroes would keep you up all the damn night, handing you that stuff about "Is it good, baby?" and "Don't you want to be my old lady?"

Talk about women getting salty when they get scorned! You should have seen Big Blue.

"What the hell good is she?" he hollered at Florence. "She's the only coloured girl in the house and she won't take Negroes?" Florence was a fine woman, but it would have been worth her life to stick up for me.

Blue knew I was a baby, but he had me busted just the same. He and Bub were real tight with the cops. The next morning I was in the kitchen with the other girls having breakfast when the cops broke in. They had stool-pigeon witnesses with them who screamed at me. "That's her," they said, pointing at me. "That's her."

So they hauled me off to jail, not for anything I did, but for something I wouldn't do. Those were rotten days. Women like Mom who worked as maids, cleaned office buildings, were picked up on the street on their way home from work and charged with prostitution. If they could pay, they got off. If they couldn't, they went to court, where it was the word of some dirty grafting cop against theirs.

They booked me and hustled me off to the Jefferson Market Court. The place was full of what they called "wayward women" in those days, and of course the vice squad fuzz. When I saw who was on the bench I knew I was cooked. It was Magistrate Jean Hortense Norris, the first woman police judge in New York, a tough hard-faced old dame with hair bobbed almost like a man's.

She had made a big name for herself, running around making sweet talk about how it took a woman to understand social problems. But I had heard from girls who had been in her court that this was all a lot of crud. She was tougher than any judge I ever saw in pants before or since. If the girls had lawyers, they'd move heaven and earth to get their cases put off to some other judge.

I knew if you pleaded guilty you caught hell. If you pleaded not guilty, you might even get worse. I didn't have anybody to get me a lawyer, not that it would have done much good. If that judge had guessed for a minute I was only fifteen she would probably have packed me off to Bedford Reformatory until I was twenty-one.

But Mom came down to court and stopped that. She swore

on a stack of Bibles I was eighteen. If they had checked up on her, it would have showed Mom had given birth to me when she was nine. But they didn't. It cost Mom a lot to tell a lie like that. She couldn't stand lying and made me the same way. She never lied unless she had to save somebody's life. And neither did I.

When my case came up, the judge picked up a piece of paper, read it off, said it was a health report that I was sick. This was pretty funny because they hadn't tested me for anything; there hadn't been time. Besides, I was clean, I knew I was clean, and the tests proved it later.

But this old girl judge didn't believe me. She read her lecture about how young I was, and how sick, and said she was going to be lenient with me and send me to a city hospital in Brooklyn. They hustled me out the way they had hustled me in. And that was that.

At the hospital they were giving everybody shots of Salvarsan for syphilis—only it was called "bad blood" then. I didn't get any shots, I gave them. I worked with the doctors and saw girls coming in with their arms eaten up from big round sores where somebody missed a vein and gave it to them in the muscle. Later I got promoted to the bismuth kick, where I used to give shots in the ass all by myself. I learned to handle those needles real good. All the girls used to ask for me because word got around that I never hurt anybody.

I might have done all my time at the hospital, but bad luck was dogging me. One night a big dike went after me. They call them lesbians now, but we just called them dikes. She tried to get at me. I took a poke at her, and down the stairs she went.

So they threw me out of the hospital after two weeks and I found myself back in the old Jefferson Market Court. The same court, the same judge, only this time she was really mad.

"I thought I was giving you a chance," she spouted at me. "But you turned out to be a girl of bad character." Wham, bang, four months she handed me, and I was off to Welfare Island.

That place was filthy. Fifty girls were packed together in one awful ward, and some of them with t.b. We got the kind of garbage to eat you wouldn't feed your dog. Every once in a while we'd all get put to work cleaning up the joint. That meant a bunch of social workers would come trooping through making an inspection. But after they'd leave, the rats would come out again and everything would slide back to filthy-dirty normal.

The rats in that place were bigger than anything I'd seen in Baltimore. And they all seemed like they'd been trained. They'd walk right past without bothering you unless they were hungry. And even if they were hungry they wouldn't bother the girls in the wards, they'd come in the kitchen just like a pet. I worked in the kitchen for a while, and there was one old rat, so beat up most of his fur was worn away, who used to come in regularly to get his chow.

All night, I'd lay awake listening to the pleasure boats going by in the East River and wonder if I'd ever get out. Like everybody else, I was just counting the days. I was supposed to get fifteen days off for good behaviour, which meant I had to count up to a hundred and five.

Then one day when I had the count down to seventy days to go, something happened that boosted my time back to eighty-five. There were plenty of dikes around that place too. And one of them had been dogging me. This day she made a pass at me, and I made a pass back with my fist. This little scuffle cost me my fifteen days off for good behaviour and caused me to get tossed in the cooler.

That place was the end—a cell so tiny there wasn't room to take one step. You had a cot, room to stand up or sit down, and that was it. No lights, it was so dark down there you lost track of night and day and had to give up counting your time. After a while you didn't even care. They gave you two pieces of bread with saltpetre in it every day and some water. I had to do ten days on that diet, but I used to throw it back in their faces.

After you got out of the cooler you were punished by getting graduated to the laundry. The girls in the laundry used to holler at me, trying to buck me up.

"Stick it out," they'd yell. "Don't throw your food away. Eat it or you'll never make it out alive."

I could hear their voices but I never got to lay eyes on a soul except the matron.

A dike was the cause of getting me in there, and another one was the cause of getting me out alive. This one matron was a chick who liked girls. I had said something to her the first time she came around and she thought I was cute. She used to sneak me a couple of cigarettes when I needed them bad, and I used to play along with her.

I knew she expected to get to make a pass at me when I got out. She expected me to be nice to her. So I didn't tell her any different. She had her own reasons for being nice to me. But any kind of freakish feelings are better than no feelings at all. If that judge had only been a dike, she might have treated me like a piece of human flesh instead of a piece of evidence. If it hadn't been for this nice dikey matron, I don't know if I would have made it.

But one day they let me out and I graduated to the laundry. My last job there was a real break—I got to cook for the warden and his family. I used to make them crazy dishes I had learned from Mom—things she used to make for rich people, like chicken cacciatore with mushrooms and roast duck. This used to knock him out. When my time was running out, he made me an offer to stay on and cook for him.

"You come to my house and I'll cook for you," I told him. "I'm never coming back here."

My job cooking for the warden made me a big shot in the joint. As a privileged character, I got to sleep in the bed by the window in the ward. Also, it meant I got out on time. They couldn't keep books on the island. Girls that were sup-

posed to do three years sometimes did three or four weeks
extra because some bookkeeper goofed. Then one day they'd
discover some girl still there who was supposed to be out.
They'd ask her what she thought she was doing. "You were
supposed to be out weeks ago," they told one girl.

But I got out right on the nose at the end of four months.
It was summer when I went in, without a stitch to my name
except my one and only silk dress and my spike-heeled patent-
leather shoes. It was winter when they let me out, and when
they checked me through the exit I got the dress, but the
chick in the check room told me she couldn't find my shoes.
I kicked up such a storm I thought they were going to keep
me there. I raised so much hell the warden finally had to
come down. When he found out what it was all about he said
my shoes had to be there someplace. He gave orders for them
to find them if they had to search the joint. The dame in the
check room found them in a hurry. She handed them over—
brand new and just her size.

So I got on that cold windy ferryboat to cross the East River
in my spike shoes and my silk dress. But it hung on me like
a prison uniform—I had dropped twenty-three pounds on the
island.

When the boat hit the shore, it seemed like half the pimps
in New York were there to meet us. They lined up at the
docks to look us over. That's their business, that's where they
auditioned their talent, and the cops did everything to make
it easy, including directing the traffic. I must have looked sad,
but there was a pimp there who gave me the "Hi, baby," and
asked me to go with him. He had a car waiting and wanted
to take me to a house right off.

I had decided I was through with hustling, but I didn't tell
him. And I had learned a lot on Welfare Island. I needed
some clothes, especially a warm winter coat. And I needed
them quick. He could get them for me. And he did.

11

FROM
Another Country
by James Baldwin
(First published 1962)

*In this excerpt from a best-selling novel, James Baldwin ex-
plores many of the conflicts that plague the black female-
white male relationship. His black protagonist, Ida—in re-
vealing her relationships with her parents, the black musicians
with whom she works, her white publicity agent Ellis, her
brother Rufus (who committed suicide), and his friends (Eric,
Richard, and Cass) as well as with other white men—brings
her relationship with Vivaldo, her white lover, to its most crucial stage: the acknowledgement of the gap their disparate
ethnic backgrounds has created between them. Baldwin also
illustrates the extreme self-degradation to which the black
woman's involvement with the white world may lead.*

IDA heard Vivaldo's step and rushed to open the door for
him, just as he began fumbling for his key. She threw back
her head and laughed.

"You look like you narrowly escaped a lynching, dad. And
where did you get that coat?" She looked him up and down,
and laughed again. "Come on in, you poor, drowned rat, before the posse gets here."

She closed the door behind him and he took off Eric's coat
and hung it in the bathroom and dried his dripping hair.
"Do we have anything to eat in this house?"

"Yes. Are you hungry?"

"Starving." He came out of the bathroom. "What did Richard have to say?"

She was in the kitchen with her back to him, digging in the cupboard beneath the sink where the pots and pans were kept. She came up with a frying pan; looked at him briefly; and this look made him feel that Richard had managed, somehow, to frighten her.

"Nothing very pleasant. But it's not important now." She put the pan on the stove and opened the icebox door. "I think you and Cass were his whole world. And now both of you have treated him so badly that he doesn't know where he is." She took tomatoes and lettuce and a package of pork chops out of the icebox and put them on the table. "He tried to make me angry—but I just felt terribly sad. He'd been so hurt." She paused. "Men are so helpless when they're hurt."

He came up behind her and kissed her. "Are they?"

She returned his kiss, and said gravely, "Yes. You don't believe it's happening. You think that there must have been some mistake."

"How wise you are!" he said.

"I'm not wise. I'm just a poor, ignorant, black girl, trying to get along. I'd sure hate like hell to tangle with one who'd made it."

"But you wouldn't know. You think women tell the truth. They don't. They can't." She stepped away from him, busy with another saucepan and water and flame. And she gave him a mocking look. "Men wouldn't *love* them if they did."

"You just don't like *men*."

She said, "I can't say that I've met very many. Not what I call men."

"I hope I'm one of them."

"Oh, there's hope for you," she said, humorously, "you might make it yet."

"That's probably," he said, "the nicest thing you've ever said to me."

She laughed, but there was something sad and lonely in the

sound. There was something sad and lonely in her whole aspect, which obscurely troubled him. And he began to watch her closely, without quite knowing that he was doing so.

She said, "Poor Vivaldo. I've given you a hard time, haven't I, baby?"

"I'm not complaining," he said, carefully.

"No," she said, half to herself, running her fingers thoughtfully through a bowl of dry rice, "I'll say that much for you. I dish it out, but you sure as hell can take it."

"You think maybe," he said, "that I take too much?"

She frowned. She dumped the rice into the boiling water. "Maybe. Hell, I don't think women know what they want, not a damn one of them. Look at Cass—do you want a drink," she asked suddenly, "before dinner?"

"Sure." He took down the bottle and the glasses and took out the ice. "What do you mean—women don't know what they want? Don't *you* know what you want?"

She had taken down the great salad bowl and was slicing tomatoes into it; it seemed that she did not dare be still. "Sure. I thought I did. I was sure once. Now I'm not so sure." She paused. "And I only found that out—last night." She looked up at him humorously, gave a little shrug, and sliced savagely into another tomato.

He set her drink beside her. "What's happened to confuse you?"

She laughed—again he heard that striking melancholy. "Living with you! Would you believe it? I fell for that jive."

He dragged his work stool in from the other room and teetered on it, watching her, a little above her.

"*What* jive, sweetheart, are you talking about?"

She sipped her drink. "That love jive, sweetheart. Love, love, love!"

His heart jumped up; they watched each other; she smiled a rueful smile. "Are you trying to tell me—without my having to ask you or anything—that you love me?"

"Am I? I guess I am." Then she dropped the knife and sat

perfectly still, looking down, the fingers of one hand drumming on the table. Then she clasped her hands, the fingers of one hand playing with the ruby-eyed snake ring, slipping it half-off, slipping it on.

"But—that's wonderful." He took her hand. It lay cold and damp and lifeless in his. A kind of wind of terror shook him for an instant. "Isn't it? It makes me very happy—*you* make me very happy."

She took his hand and rested her cheek against it. "Do I, Vivaldo?" Then she rose and walked to the sink to wash the lettuce.

He followed her, standing beside her, and looking into her closed, averted face. "What's the matter, Ida?" He put one hand on her waist; she shivered, as if in revulsion, and he let his hand fall. "Tell me, please."

"It's nothing," she said, trying to sound light about it. "I told you, I'm in a bad mood. It's probably the time of the month."

"Now, come on, baby, don't try to cop out that way."

She was tearing the lettuce and washing it, and placing it in a towel. She continued with this in silence, until she had torn off the last leaf. She was trying to avoid his eyes; he had never seen her at such a loss before. Again, he was frightened. "What *is* it?"

"Leave me alone, Vivaldo. We'll talk about it later."

"We will *not* talk about it later. We'll talk about it now."

The rice came to a boil and she moved hastily away from him to turn down the flame.

"My Mama always told me, honey, you can't cook and talk."

"Well, stop *cooking!*"

She gave him that look, coquettish, wide-eyed, and amused, which he had known so long. But now there was something desperate in it; had there always been something desperate in this look? "But you *said* you were hungry!"

"Stop that. It's not funny, okay?" He led her to the table.

"I want to know what's happening. Is it something Richard said?"

"I am not trying to be funny. I *would* like to feed you." Then, with a sudden burst of anger, "It's got nothing to do with Richard. What, after all, can Richard *say?*"

He had had some wild idea that Richard had made up a story about himself and Eric, and he had been on the point of denying it. He recovered, hoping that she had not been aware of his panic; but his panic increased.

He said, very gently, "Well, then, what *is* it, Ida?"

She said, wearily, "Oh, it's too many things, it goes too far back, I can never make you understand it, never."

"Try me. You say you love me. Why can't you trust me?"

She laughed. "Oh. You think life is so simple." She looked up at him and laughed again. And this laughter was unbearable. He wanted to strike her, not in anger, only to make the laughter stop; but he forced himself to stand still, and did nothing. "Because—I know you're older than I am—I always think of you as being much younger. I always think of you as being a very nice boy who doesn't know what the score is, who'll maybe never find out. And I don't want to be the one to teach you."

She said the last in a venomous undertone, looking down again at her hands.

"Okay. Go on."

"Go *on?*" She looked up at him in a strange, wild way. "You want me to go *on?*"

He said, "Please stop tormenting me, Ida. Please go on."

"*Am* I tormenting you?"

"You want it in writing?"

Her face changed, she rose from the table and walked back to the stove. "I'm sure it must seem like that to you," she said—very humbly. She moved to the sink and leaned against it, watching him. "But I wasn't trying to torment you—whenever I did. I don't think that I thought about that at all. In fact, I know I didn't, I've never had the time." She watched his face. "I've just realized lately that I've bitten off more than I can chew, certainly more than I can swallow." He winced. She broke off suddenly: "Are you sure you're a man, Vivaldo?"

He said, "I've got to be sure."

"Fair enough," she said. She walked to the stove and put a light under the frying pan, walked to the table and opened the meat. She began to dust it with salt and pepper and paprika, and chopped garlic into it, near the bone. He took a swallow of his drink, which had no taste whatever; he splashed more whiskey into his glass. "When Rufus died, something happened to me," she said. She sounded now very quiet and weary, as though she were telling someone else's story; also, as though she herself, with a faint astonishment, were hearing it for the first time. But it was yet more astonishing that he now began to listen to a story he had always known, but never dared believe. "I can't explain it. Rufus had always been the world to me. I loved him."

"So did I," he said—too quickly, irrelevantly; and for the first time it occurred to him that, possibly, he was a liar; had never loved Rufus at all, but had only feared and envied him.

"I don't need your credentials, Vivaldo," she said.

She watched the frying pan critically, waiting for it to become hot enough, then dropped in a little oil. "The point, anyway, at the moment, is that *I* loved him. He was my big brother, but as soon as I knew anything, I knew that I was stronger than he was. He was nice, he was really very nice, no matter what any of you might have thought of him later. None of you, anyway, knew anything about him, you didn't know how."

"You often say that," he said, wearily. "Why?"

"How could you—how *can* you?—dreaming the way you dream? You people think you're free. That means you think you've got something other people want—or need. Shit." She grinned wryly and looked at him. "And you *do*, in a way. But it isn't what you think it is. And you're going to find

out, too, just as soon as some of those other people start getting what you've got now." She shook her head. "I feel sorry
for them. I feel sorry for you. I even feel kind of sorry for myself, because God knows I've often wished you'd left me
where I was—"

"Down there in the jungle?" he taunted.

"Yes. Down there in the jungle, black and funky—and myself."

His small anger died down as quickly as it had flared up.
"Well," he said, quietly, "sometimes I'm nostalgic, too, Ida."
He watched her dark, lonely face. For the first time, he had
an intimation of how she would look when she grew old.
"What I've never understood," he said, finally, "is that you
always accuse me of making a thing about your color, of
penalizing you. But you do the same thing. You always make
me feel white. Don't you think that hurts me? You lock me
out. And all I want is for you to be a part of me, for me to be
a part of you. I wouldn't give a damn if you were striped
like a zebra."

She laughed. "Yes, you would, really. But you say the
cutest things." Then, "if I lock you out, as you put it, it's
mainly to protect you—"

"Protect me from what? and I don't *want* to be protected.
Besides—"

"Besides?"

"I don't believe you. I don't believe that's why. You want
to protect yourself. You want to hate me because I'm white,
because it's easier for you that way."

"I don't hate you."

"Then why do you always bring it up? What *is* it?"

She stirred the rice, which was almost ready, found a colander, and placed it in the sink. Then she turned to face him.

"This all began because I said that you people—"

"Listen to yourself. *You people!*"

"—didn't know anything about Rufus—"

"Because we're white."

"No. Because he was black."

"Oh. I give *up*. And anyway, why must we always end up talking about Rufus?"

"I had started to tell you something," she said, quietly; and watched him.

He swallowed some more of his whiskey, and lit a cigarette. "True. Please go on."

"*Because* I'm black," she said, after a moment, and sat at the table near him, "I know more about what happened to my brother than you can ever know. I watched it happen—from the beginning. I was there. He shouldn't have ended up the way he did. That's what's been so hard for me to accept. He was a very beautiful boy. Most people aren't beautiful, I knew that right away. I watched them, and I knew. But he didn't because he was so much nicer than I." She paused, and the silence grumbled with the sound of the frying pan and the steady sound of the rain. "He loved our father, for example. He really loved him. I didn't. He was just a loud-mouthed, broken-down man, who liked to get drunk and hang out in barber shops—well, maybe he didn't like it but that was all he could find to do, except work like a dog, for nothing—and play the guitar on the week ends for his only son." She paused again, smiling. "There was something very nice about those week ends, just the same. I can still see Daddy, his belly hanging out, strumming on that guitar and trying to teach Rufus some down-home song and Rufus grinning at him and making fun of him a little, really, but very nicely, and singing with him. I bet my father was never happier, all the days of his life, than when he was singing for Rufus. He's got no one to sing to now. He was so proud of him. He bought Rufus his first set of drums."

She was not locking him out now; he felt, rather, that he was being locked in. He listened, seeing, or trying to see, what she saw, and feeling something of what she felt. But he wondered, just the same, how much her memory had filtered out. And he wondered what Rufus must have looked like in those

days, with all his bright, untried brashness, and all his hopes
intact.

She was silent for a moment, leaning forward, looking
down, her elbows on her knees and the fingers of one hand
restlessly playing with her ring.

"When Rufus died, all the light went out of that house, all
of it. That was why I couldn't stay there. I knew I couldn't
stay there, I'd grow old like they were, suddenly, and I'd end
up like all the other abandoned girls who can't find anyone to
protect them. I'd always known I couldn't end up like that,
I'd always known it. I'd counted on Rufus to get me out of
there—I knew he'd do anything in the world for me, just like
I would for him. It hadn't occurred to me that it wouldn't
happen. I *knew* it would happen."

She rose and returned to the stove and took the rice off the
fire and poured it into the colander and ran water over it;
put water in the saucepan and put it back on the fire, placing
the colander on top of it and covering the rice with a towel.
She turned the chops over. Then she sat down.

"When we saw Rufus's body, I can't tell you. My father
stared at it, he stared at it, and stared at it. It didn't look like
Rufus, it was—terrible—from the salt water, and he must have
struck something going down, or in the water, because he was
so broken and lumpy—and ugly. *My* brother. And my father
stared at it—at it—and he said, They don't leave a man much,
do they? His own father was beaten to death with a hammer
by a railroad guard. And they brought his father home like
that. My mother got frightened, she wanted my father to
pray. And he said, he shouted it at the top of his lungs, Pray?
Who, pray? I bet you, if I ever get anywhere near that white
devil you call God, I'll tear my son and my father out of his
white hide! Don't you never say the word Pray to me again,
woman, not if you want to *live.* Then he started to cry. I'll
never forget it. Maybe I hadn't loved him before, but I
loved him then. That was the last time he ever shouted, he
hasn't raised his voice since. He just sits there, he doesn't

even drink any more. Sometimes he goes out and listens to those fellows who make speeches on 125th Street and Seventh Avenue. He says he just wants to live long enough—long enough—"

Vivaldo said, to break the silence which abruptly roared around them, "To be paid back."

"Yes," she said. "And I felt that way, too."

She walked over to the stove again.

"I felt that I'd been robbed. And I *had* been robbed—of the only hope I had. By a group of people too cowardly even to know what they had done. And it didn't seem to me that they deserved any better than what they'd given me. I didn't care what happened to them, just so they suffered. I didn't really much care what happened to me. But I wasn't going to let what happened to Rufus, and what was happening all around me, happen to me. I was going to get through the world, and get what I needed out of it, no matter how."

He thought, *Oh, it's coming now,* and felt a strange, bitter relief. He finished his drink and lit another cigarette, and watched her.

She looked over at him, as though to make certain that he was still listening.

"Nothing you've said so far," he said, carefully, "seems to have much to do with being black. Except for what you make out of it. But nobody can help you there."

She sighed sharply, in a kind of rage. "That could be true. But it's too easy for you to say that."

"Ida, a lot of what you've had to say, ever since we met, has been—too easy." He watched her. "Hasn't it?" And then, "Sweetheart, suffering doesn't *have* a color. Does it? Can't we step out of this nightmare? I'd give anything. I'd give anything if we could." He crossed to her and took her in his arms. "Please, Ida, whatever has to be done, to set us free—let's do that."

Her eyes were full of tears. She looked down. "Let me finish my story."

"Nothing you say will make any difference."

"You don't know that. Are you afraid?"

He stepped back. "No." Then, "Yes. Yes. I can't take any more of your revenge."

"Well, I can't either. Let me finish."

"Come away from the stove. I can't eat now."

"Everything will be ruined."

"Let it be ruined. Come and sit down."

He wished that he were better prepared for this moment, that he had not been with Eric, that his hunger would vanish, that his fear would drop, and love lend him a transcendent perception and concentration. But he knew himself to be physically weak and tired, not drunk, but far from sober; part of his troubled mind was far away, gorging on the conundrum of himself.

She put out the fire under the frying pan and came and sat at the table. He pushed her drink toward her, but she did not touch it.

"I knew there wasn't any hope uptown. A lot of those men, they got their little deals going and all that, but they don't really have anything. Mr. Charlie's not going to let them get but so far. Those that really do have something would never have any use for me; I'm too dark for them, they see girls like me on Seventh Avenue every day. I knew what they would do to me."

And now he knew that he did not want to hear the rest of her story. He thought of himself on Seventh Avenue; perhaps he had never left. He thought of the day behind him, of Eric and Cass and Richard, and felt himself now being sucked into the rapids of a mysterious defeat.

"There was only one thing for me to do, as Rufus used to say, and that was to hit the A train. So I hit it. Nothing was clear in my mind at first. I used to see the way white men watched me, like dogs. And I thought about what I could do to them. How I hated them, the way they looked, and the things they'd say, all dressed up in their damn white skin, and their clothes just so, and their little weak, white pricks jumping in their drawers. You could do any damn thing with them if you just led them along, because they wanted to do something dirty and they knew that you knew how. All black people knew that. Only, the polite ones didn't say dirty. They said real. I used to wonder what in the world they did in bed, white people, I mean, between themselves, to get them so sick. Because they *are* sick, and I'm telling you something that I know. I had a couple of girl friends and we used to go out every once in a while with some of these shitheads. But they were smart, too, they knew that they were white, and they could always go back home, and there wasn't a damn thing you could do about it. I thought to myself, Shit, this scene is not for me. Because I didn't want their little change, I didn't want to be at their mercy. I wanted them to be at mine."

She sipped her drink.

"Well, you were calling me all the time about that time, but I didn't really think about you very much, not seriously anyway. I liked you, but I certainly hadn't planned to get hung up on a white boy who didn't have any money—in fact, I hadn't planned to get hung up on anybody. But I liked you, and the few times I saw you it was a kind of—*relief*—from all those other, horrible people. You were really nice to me. You didn't have that look in your eyes. You just acted like a real sweet boy and maybe, without knowing it, I got to depend on it. Sometimes I'd just see you for a minute or so, we'd just have a cup of coffee or something like that, and I'd run off— but I felt better, I was kind of protected from their eyes and their hands. I was feeling so sick most of the time through there. I didn't want my father to know what I was doing and I tried not to think about Rufus. That was when I decided that I ought to try to sing, I'd do it for Rufus, and then all the rest wouldn't matter. I would have settled the score. But I thought I needed somebody to help me, and it was then, just at that time that I—" She stopped and looked down at her hands. "I think I wanted to go to bed with you, not to

have an affair with you, but just to go to bed with somebody
that I *liked*. Somebody who wasn't old, because all those men
are old, no matter how young they are. I'd only been to bed
with one boy I liked, a boy on our block, but he got religion,
and so it all stopped and he got married. And there weren't
any other colored men. I was afraid, because look what happened to them, they got cut down like grass! And I didn't
see any way out, except—finally—you. And Ellis."

Then she stopped. They listened to the rain. He had finished his drink and he picked up hers. She looked down, he
had the feeling that she could not look up, and he was afraid
to touch her. And the silence stretched; he longed for it to
end, and dreaded it; there was nothing he could say.

She straightened her shoulders and reached out for a cigarette. He lit it for her.

"Richard knows about me and Ellis," she said in a matter-
of-fact tone, "but that's not why I'm telling you. I'm telling
you because I'm trying to bring this whole awful thing to a
halt. If that's possible."

She paused. She said, "Let me have a sip of your drink,
please."

"It's yours," he said. He gave it to her and poured himself
another one.

She blew a cloud of smoke toward the ceiling. "It's funny
the way things work. If it hadn't been for you, I don't think
Ellis would ever have got so hung up on me. *He* saw, better
than I did, that I really liked you and that meant that I could
really like somebody and so why not him, since he could give
me so much more? And I thought so, too, that it was a kind of
dirty trick for life to play on me, for me to like you better
than I liked him. And, after all, the chances of its lasting were
just about equal, only with him, if I played it right, I might
have something to show for it when it was all over. And he
was smart, he didn't bug me about it, he said, Sure, he wanted
me but he was going to help me, regardless, and the one
thing had nothing to do with the other. And he did—he was

very nice to me, in his way, he was as good as his word, he was nicer to me than anyone had ever been before. He used to take me out to dinner, to places where nobody would know him or where it wouldn't matter if they did. A lot of the time we went up to Harlem, or if he knew I was sitting in somewhere, he'd drop in. He didn't seem to be trying to hype me, not even when he talked about his wife and his kids—you know? He sounded as though he really *was* lonely. And, after all, I owed him a lot—and—it was nice to be treated that way and to know the cat had enough money to take you anywhere, and—ah! well, it started, I guess I'd always known it was going to start, and then, once it started, I didn't think I could stand it but I didn't know how to stop it. Because it's one thing for a man to be doing all these things for you while you're not having an affair with him and it's another thing for him to be doing them after you've *stopped* having an affair with him. And I had to go on, I had to get up there on top, where maybe I could begin to breathe. But I saw why he'd never been upset about you. He really is smart. He was *glad* I was with you, he told me so; he was glad I had another boy friend because it made it easier for him. It meant I wouldn't make any scenes, I wouldn't think I'd fallen in love with him. It gave him another kind of power over me in a way because he knew that I was afraid of your finding out and the more afraid I got, the harder it was to refuse him. Do you understand that?"

"Yes," he said, slowly, "I think I understand that."

They stared at each other. She dropped her eyes.

"But, you know," she said, slowly, "I think you knew all the time."

He said nothing. She persisted, in a low voice, "Didn't you?"

"You told me that you weren't," he said.

"But did you believe me?"

He stammered: "I—I *had* to believe you."

"Why?"

Again, he said nothing.

"Because you were afraid?"

"Yes," he said at last. "I was afraid."

"It was easier to let it happen than to try to stop it?"

"Yes."

"Why?"

Her eyes searched his face. It was his turn to look away.

"I used to hate you for that sometimes," she said, "for pretending to believe me because you didn't want to know what was happening to me."

"I was trying to do what I thought you wanted! I was afraid that you would *leave* me—you *told* me that you would!" He rose and stalked the kitchen, his hands in his pockets, water standing in his eyes. "I worried about it, I thought about it—but I put it out of my mind. You had made it a matter of my trusting you—don't you remember?"

He looked at her with hatred, standing above her; but she seemed to be beyond his anger.

"Yes, I remember. But you didn't start trusting me. You just gave in to me and pretended to trust me."

"What would you have done if I had called you on it?"

"I don't know. But if you had faced it, I would have had to face it—as long as you were pretending, I had to pretend. I'm not blaming you. I'm just telling it to you like it is." She looked up at him. "I saw that it could go on a long time like that," and her lips twisted wearily. "I sort of had you where I wanted you. I'd got my revenge. Only, it wasn't *you* I was after. It wasn't *you* I was trying to beat."

"It was Ellis?"

She sighed and put one hand to her face. "Oh. I don't know, I really don't know what I was thinking. Sometimes I'd leave Ellis and I'd come and find you here—like my dog or my cat, I used to think sometimes, just waiting. And I'd be afraid you'd be here and I'd be afraid you'd gone out, afraid you'd ask me, *really* ask me where I'd been, and afraid you wouldn't. Sometimes you'd try, but I could always stop you, I could see in your eyes when you were frightened. I hated that look and I hated me and I hated you. I could see how white men got that look they so often had when they looked at me; somebody had beat the shit out of them, had scared the shit out of them, long ago. And now I was doing it to you. And it made it hard for me when you touched me, especially—" She stopped, picked up her drink, tasted it, set it down. "I couldn't stand Ellis. You don't know what it's like, to have a man's body over you if you can't stand that body. And it was worse now, since I'd been with you, than it had ever been before. Before, I used to watch them wriggle and listen to them grunt, and, God, they were so solemn about it, sweating yellow pigs, and so *vain,* like that sad little piece of meat was making miracles happen, and I guess it was, for them—and I wasn't touched at all, I just wished I could make them come down lower. Oh, yes, I found out all about white people, *that's* what they were like, alone, where only a black girl could see them, and the black girl might as well have been blind as far as they were concerned. Because they knew they were white, baby, and they ruled the world. But now it was different, sometimes when Ellis put his hands on me, it was all I could do not to scream, not to vomit. It had *got* to me, it had got *to* me, and I felt that I was being pumped full of—I don't know what, not poison exactly, but dirt, *waste,* filth, and I'd never be able to get it out of me, never be able to get that stink out of me. And sometimes, sometimes, some-times—" She covered her mouth, her tears spilled down over her hand, over the red ring. He could not move. "Oh, Lord Jesus. I've done terrible things. Oh, Lord. Sometimes. And then I'd come home to you. He always had that funny little smile when I finally left him, that smile he has, I've seen it many times now, when he's outsmarted somebody who doesn't know it yet. He can't help it, that's him, it was as though he were saying, 'Now that I'm through with you, have a nice time with Vivaldo. And give him my regards.' And, funny, funny—I couldn't hate him. I saw what he was doing, but I couldn't hate him. I wondered what it felt like, to be like that, not to have any real feelings at all, except to say, Well, now, let's do this and now let's do that and now let's eat and now let's fuck and now let's go. And do that all your life. And then I'd come home and look at you. But I'd bring him with me. It was as though I was dirty, and you had to wash me, each time. And I knew you never could, no matter how hard we tried, and I didn't hate him but I hated you. And I hated me."

"Why didn't you stop it, Ida? You could have stopped it, you didn't have to go on with it."

"Stop it and go where? Stop it and do what? No, I thought, to myself, Well, you're in it now, girl, close your eyes and grit your teeth and get through it. It'll be worth it when it's over. And that's why I've been working so hard. To get away."

"And what about me? What about us?"

She looked up at him with a bitter smile. "What about us? I hoped I'd get through this and then we'd see. But last night something happened, I couldn't take it any more. We were up at Small's Paradise—"

"Last night? You and Ellis?"

"Yes. *And* Cass."

"Cass?"

"I asked her to come and have a drink with me."

"Did you leave together?"

"No."

"So that's why she got in late last night." He looked at her. "It's a good thing I didn't come home then, isn't it?"

"What would you have done," she cried, "if you had? You'd have sat at that typewriter for a while and then you'd have played some music and then you'd have gone out and got drunk. And when I came home, no matter *when* I came home, you'd have believed any lie I told you because you were afraid not to."

"What a bitch you are," he said.

"Yes," she said, with a terrible sobriety, "I know." She lit a cigarette. The hand that held the match trembled. "But I'm trying not to be. I don't know if there's any hope for me or not." She dropped the match on the table. "He made me sing with the band. They didn't really want me to, and I didn't want to, but they didn't want to say No, to him. So I sang. And of course I knew some of the musicians and some of them had known Rufus. Baby, if musicians don't want to work with you, they sure can make you know it. I sang *Sweet Georgia Brown,* and something else. I wanted to get off that stand in the worst way. When it was over, and the people were clapping, the bass player whispered to me, he said, 'You black white man's whore, don't you never let me catch you on Seventh Avenue, you hear? I'll tear your little black pussy *up.*' And the other musicians could hear him, and they were grinning. 'I'm going to do it twice, once for every black man you castrate every time you walk, and once for your poor brother, because I loved that stud. And he going to thank me for it, too, you can bet on that, black girl.' And he slapped me on the ass, hard, everybody could see it and, you know, those people up there aren't fools, and before I could get away, he grabbed my hand and raised it, and he said, 'She's the *champion,* ain't she, folks? Talk about walking, this girl ain't *started* walking!' And he dropped my hand, hard, like it was too hot or too dirty, and I almost fell off the stand. And everybody laughed and cheered, they knew what he meant, and I did, too. And I got back to the table. Ellis was grinning like it was all a big joke. And it was. On me."

She rose, and poured herself a fresh drink.

"Then he took me to that place he has, way over on the East River. I kept wondering what I was going to do. I didn't know what to do. I watched his face in the taxicab. He put his hand on my leg. And he tried to take my hand. But I couldn't move. I kept thinking of what that black man had said to me, and his face when he said it, and I kept thinking of Rufus, and I kept thinking of you. It was like a merry-go-round, all these faces just kept going around in my mind. And a song kept going around in my head, *Oh, Lord, is it I?*

And there he sat, next to me, puffing on his cigar. The funny thing was that I knew if I really started crying or pleading, he'd take me home. He can't stand scenes. But I couldn't even do that. And God knows I wanted to get home, I hoped you wouldn't be here, so I could just crawl under the sheets and die. And, that way, when you came home, I could tell you everything before you came to bed, and—maybe—but, no, we were going to his place and I felt that I deserved it. I felt that I couldn't fall much lower, I might as well go all the way and get it over with. And then we'd see, if there was anything left of me after that, we'd see." She threw down about two fingers of whiskey and immediately poured herself another drink. "There's always farther to fall, always, always." She moved from the table, holding her glass, and leaned against the ice-box door. "And I did everything he wanted, I let him have his way. It wasn't me. It wasn't me." She gestured aimlessly with her glass, tried to drink from it, dropped it, and suddenly fell on her knees beside the table, her hands against her belly, weeping.

Stupidly, he picked up the glass, afraid that she would cut herself. She was kneeling in the spilled whiskey, which had stained the edges of her skirt. He dropped the broken glass in the brown paper bag they used for garbage. He was afraid to go near her, he was afraid to touch her, it was almost as though she had told him that she had been infected with the plague. His arms trembled with his revulsion, and every act of the body seemed unimaginably vile. And yet, at the same time, as he stood helpless and stupid in the kitchen which had abruptly become immortal, or which, in any case, would surely live as long as he lived, and follow him everywhere, his heart began to beat with a newer, stonier anguish, which destroyed the distance called pity and placed him, very nearly, in her body, beside the table on the dirty floor. The single yellow light beat terribly down on them both. He went to her, his belly sore. And, nevertheless, for a moment, he could not touch her, he did not know how. He thought, unwillingly, of all the whores, black whores, with whom he had coupled, and what he had hoped for from them, and he was gripped in a kind of restrospective nausea. What would they see when they looked into each other's faces again? "Come on, Ida," he whispered, "come on, Ida. Get up," and at last he touched her shoulders, trying to force her to rise. She tried to check her sobs, she put both hands on the table.

"I'm all right," she murmured, "give me a handkerchief."

He knelt beside her, and thrust his handkerchief, warm and wadded, but fairly clean, into her hand. She blew her nose. He kept his arm around her shoulder. "Stand up," he said. "Go wash your face. Would you like some coffee?"

||||

BLACK ON BLACK:

THE BLACK WOMAN
IN THE BLACK WORLD

PREPONDERANTLY the black woman's experiences are of the black community itself—in rural shacks or ghetto tenements or even in the staid suburban replicas of middle-class white living. But the peculiar and exploitative relationship black females have had with the white world, particularly its males, has necessarily affected her relationships with her own people. It is not surprising, then, that as lover, wife, mother, and grandmother she has adopted attitudes and postures distinctly different than those common in white middle-class society.

Perhaps the most disastrous consequence of the American legacy in regard to the black woman has been the wedge driven between her and the black male. The rancor and low esteem developed on both sides as a result of the black male's position in America and the black female's usurpation of elements of the masculine role have wrecked many black families. The alternative has been an uneasy truce, in which both male and female spar continually in an attempt to resolve the environmentally induced pressures that plague them. Moreover, when those pressures force a rift, even a temporary one, the black woman's inclination has been towards a more intense pursuit of the dominating, matriarchal life style which many sociologists are now discovering in black communities.

The selections that follow illustrate the complexity—both the richness and poverty—of the black woman's experiences in relating to black men, building a stable family, and avoiding the pitfalls that pervade the adverse environment in which she exists.

1

FROM

The Mark of Oppression

by Abram Kardiner, M.D., and Lionel Ovesey, M.D.
(First published 1951)

*Usually broken homes occur more frequently among poor or
lower-class families, but the incidence of broken homes
among poor non-whites is greater than in any other segment of
our society. In 1964, while less than five per cent of the husbands of white women were absent, among non-whites more
than twenty per cent were absent. In the following selection,
a sociological report taken from a chapter entitled "Negro
Adaptation: A Psycho-dynamic Analysis," the higher occur-
rence rate of marital breakups among blacks is analyzed. Although some of the conclusions reached here are perhaps over-
generalized, the psychological effect of family dissolution on
the black female is clearly described. Also the authors clarify
the relationship between poverty and broken families, and
point out the cyclical nature of that relationship.*

THE BROKEN HOME

In discussing the broken home as one of the expressions of
Negro personality, we seem to commit the error of using it
both as a cause and as an effect. This is not an error. It is the
kind of cycle that is easily demonstrable in any culture. Beginning in Alor [1] with maternal neglect, we can trace the ef-

1. In 1944 Cora Du Bois published *The People of Alor,* an in-depth analysis
of the social structure of the inhabitants on the island of Alor in the Nether-

fects of this in the individual so that when the child becomes a mother she then repeats the same thing; she neglects and rejects her children. This is not an imitative process by any means; it is the end result of an integrative process.

The broken home in the lower-class family is very commonly attributed to the precarious economic conditions under which these families live. This statement is not untrue; it is merely incomplete. No single factor operates in such direct line to so complex an end product as the broken home. This is the culmination of a large number of factors, each of which adds to the momentum of the rest.

Let us begin arbitrarily somewhere in the cycle, with the father who abandons his wife and offspring. On the face of it, this is very easy to explain by merely saying that the father has no sense of responsibility, and since this is a very reprehensible trait, the Negro male bears the brunt of the accusation. Moreover, since this is generally considered a character trait of the Negro—presumably of racial origin—that seems to settle the matter. Our researches in personality do not bear out this trite conclusion.

More often than not, the father who abandons his children was himself the product of a broken home, which means that he never had the patient care of a father to whom he, as a child, could look for protection and take as an ideal. On the contrary, he was generally in the custody of some foster parent who treated him cruelly; he commonly had violent sibling rivalry with step-siblings and usually got the worst of it. His mother, if she cared for him, had to work and was generally irritable and demanded immediate obedience. He never received tender and affectionate care. The end result of these factors is that he grew up to think little of himself, to expect nothing but frustrations from his mother and siblings; he trusted no one and his capacity for cooperative affectivity was severely damaged in the whole process. In addition to all this,

---

lands Antilles. Her description and analysis of this culture has since been used by sociologists, anthropologists and psychiatrists as a basis of comparison for studying other cultures. [Editor's footnote]

he did not grow up with a very exalted ideal of masculinity, which he heard repeatedly disparaged by his female relatives who, to be sure, were the mainstays of his life.

Here, another factor enters to make a contribution to the damage. His mother image is not an affectionate and loving one; it is harsh and demanding; the woman is one toward whom he seems foredoomed to take a submissive attitude, contrary to the commonly accepted ideal. This spoils his sexual attitude. He may or may not emerge with some gross sexual disturbance, like impotence. But he surely comes out of it with a disturbed, unconfident, untrusting attitude. If he marries, he knows the woman has much better economic chances than he has. Then, his position in the home is already jeopardized by his preparation for submissiveness to her—in our male-oriented society.

With this as a preparation, he enters marriage, usually impulsively. Neither he nor his spouse have any great tolerance for mutual incompatibilities. Now come the vicissitudes of employment. If he finds work, it is hardly ever permament, nor does it last for long periods. Or he must go to another city in search of work. He tries, and in many instances tries very hard, to live up to his obligations. But he cannot do so and he fails continuously. It is at this point that the dissatisfied wife takes a hand at berating and browbeating—and often invites him to leave—or he leaves at the end of a long saga of frustrated efforts.

The antagonism in the broken home is mostly due to the incapacity of both mates for continuous relatedness. There is generally fear and suspicion on both sides. Several of the males we studied continued for long periods to have tender feelings for their children; but few retain much for the wife. Not infrequently, the deserter gets a job in another city, gets caught up in serious debts, and begs and borrows—in addition to working hard—to pay them back. These harassed men often go on sprees, for a bit of self-indulgence, or spend out of proportion for their clothes, to bolster their fallen morale. The deserter is not generally a vindictive or self-righteous figure. He is generally a very defeated person, who now tries to drown his sorrows in drink or in a not very abandoned hedonism with women, to whom he can discharge his obligations with money—which means more indebtedness, etc., etc. . . .

Let us consider the instance of the male who does not desert the family, but stays on and lets his wife take up the slack. She works to supply the main support of the family while his sporadic earnings help occasionally. He is now definitely subordinate to his wife. Some of the histories indicate that under these conditions the man is submissive and unassertive, or he is overassertive and domineering over his children.

The abandoned wife usually tries marriage a second time. Meanwhile, she leads a harassed existence between work and caring for her young. Generally, she tries to do this herself. Her mother, if alive, is frequently helpful. Failing this, a sister or a brother takes the child, where he is not wanted and he is exposed to bitter rivalries with other children. The second marriage is commonly undertaken in the hope of relieving her economic distress. Often she succeeds the second time. Should this fail, she is then completely disillusioned and hopes for little from marriage. Her lot, from this point on, is hopeless and incessant toil. Most of the time she is not able to give her children either satisfactions or love. There are, of course, many exceptions.

The effects of this general situation on the children is catastrophic—in comparison with what happens in the middle-class white or Negro home. These factors, mentioned below, do not concern the fate of a single individual. What happens is a major concern of the entire community, because the total fabric of social relatedness is undermined—at least for the kind of society we live in. The following constellations are affected:

The affectivity potential is lowered.

The paternal ideal is disparaged.

The maternal ideal is injured.

The sexual or male-female relationship is spoiled.

The conscience mechanisms suffer.

The self-esteem systems suffer.

The capacity for idealization is destroyed, partially or wholly.

The potentiality for parenthood is spoiled.

The deserting or improvident father serves as a poor ideal for his children. Many of the females in this group remember the father without any fondness, chiefly as a punishing figure. These women grow up to fear and distrust men. Their sexual attitude to men suffers and the number of gross sexual disorders in this group is astonishingly high. We see none of the expected sexual hedonism. The greatest damage to the group as a whole is done by the injury in the boy's mental life to his paternal ideal. He never hears his father's role lauded, only condemned. The common imprecations are indolence, good-for-nothingness, and moral lassitude.

The male child, whose parental ideals have thus been injured, takes to the streets. Here, he has his own world, his group morality, loyalties, and animosities. It is action and adventure. Here is a chance for elevating self-esteem, of performing exploits that give pride, and of letting off steam on the hostile world or on those delegated to represent it. Here, there is also the chance to be a "man" with the girls. There is a great deal more that the boy gets from the streets that he cannot get at home; he gets praise, admiration, pride in achievement, cooperation and competition, hero-worship, confidence. It does not matter to him, nor does he know, that he has bought these satisfactions at the cost of engaging in activities that are antisocial. The maternal ideal, however, in most of these adolescents, has a permanent restraining influence for the better. The mother is, for the greater part, feared and respected, but not especially loved. Thus far, the only decisive influences toward ideal-formation have come from an ambivalent mother-image and from the street gangs. This is not a firm basis for lasting self-confidence.

On top of all this, now add the never escapable effects of caste. What equipment do either boy or girl have for effective parenthood? And so the vicious circle is endlessly repeated.

MALE-FEMALE RELATIONS

It is not commonly recognized that the poor relations between male and female in the lower classes is a serious disrupting influence. This tension between the sexes is not a calculated or a "cultural" trait; it is an accidental by-product. The importance of peaceful and cooperative attitudes between the sexes, together with mutual acceptance of the established social role for each, is a factor that has endless repercussions in either the smooth or the disorganized functioning of a society. This tension cannot be kept private or quiet; ultimately, it always takes on an expressive and public form.

The origin of this tension lies in a single factor in Negro lower-class life, a factor that is blatant in all employment statistics. These show clearly that the male has fewer and less enduring chances for permanent employment. In the actual practice of living, this is a factor of astonishing regularity in the life of any lower-class male.

This disparity of economic chances today has a long history among the Negro people. In the slave years, the female had a higher use-value to the group, because of her sexual value to the white male. She was the only member of the group who was capable of entering into some emotional reciprocity with her white masters, as mistress, as mother of lighter-skinned Negroes, and as mammy to the white children. The Negro male slave only had utility value; the female had this, and a sexual and emotional value as well. This gave her a head start in relative prestige, while that of the Negro male fell. She always did and still does remain the most permanent and dependable member of Negro society—insofar as the children are concerned.

For entirely different reasons, the free Negro female has

retained her prestige, but now because of her better chances for employment. This heightened prestige and dependability does not remain an isolated phenomenon. Its influence spreads into the ideal-formation of the children and in the sexual attitudes of male and female to each other. What is the result? The female now has some of the social value attributes of the male, and the male those of the female. The lower-class Negro female cannot be "feminine," nor the male "masculine." Their roles are reversed. Since these values are just the opposite from what they are in white society, and since the values of white society are inescapable, the male fears and hates the female; the female mistrusts and has contempt for the male because he cannot validate his nominal masculinity in practice.

This becomes a tension point in the social and sexual relations between the two, which is a powerful factor in disrupting lower-class marriage. As a submissive and dependent object, the male cannot have any pride; and whether she has pride or not, the female carries the bigger load of responsibility. This means that the male must seek compensations for his defeat in other ways: clothing, spending, gambling, drugs, extramarital sexual conquests, and other self-validating pursuits. To the female, it means the devaluation of the sexual role and a dedication to ceaseless toil and unrewarding responsibilities.

It is, therefore, no surprise that in the lower classes there should be such a high proportion of sexual disorders in both sexes.

2

"The Ethics of Living Jim Crow"

by Richard Wright
(First published 1940)

FROM

Uncle Tom's Children

Ironically, the black woman's attempt to protect her children from the hostile white world has conspired to perpetuate the cycle of broken families discussed in the previous selection. The harsh, demanding mother-image commonly adopted to thwart a young boy's natural, but dangerous, impulse to resist racial prejudice prepares the child to accept a submissive role with women and, if the mother is especially forceful, to distort his masculine adjustment to society. This excerpt from Richard Wright's autobiographical essays, in which a mother gives her son the dictum that he was "never, never, under any circumstances, to fight white folks," illuminates the insecurity and fear that black women have felt compelled to implant in their children. This insecurity has often led to erratic or "irresponsible" behavior among black males, and thereby increased the incidence of broken homes in black communities.

MY FIRST lesson in how to live as a Negro came when I was quite small. We were living in Arkansas. Our house stood behind the railroad tracks. Its skimpy yard was paved with black cinders. Nothing green ever grew in that yard. The only touch of green we could see was far away, beyond the tracks, over where the white folks lived. But cinders were good enough for me and I never missed the green growing things. And anyhow cinders were fine weapons. You could always have a nice hot war with huge black cinders. All you had to do was crouch behind the brick pillars of a house with your hands full of gritty ammunition. And the first woolly black head you saw pop out from behind another row of pillars was your target. You tried your very best to knock it off. It was great fun.

I never fully realized the appalling disadvantages of a cinder environment till one day the gang to which I belonged found itself engaged in a war with the white boys who lived beyond the tracks. As usual we laid down our cinder barrage, thinking that this would wipe the white boys out. But they replied with a steady bombardment of broken bottles. We doubled our cinder barrage, but they hid behind trees, hedges, and the sloping embankments of their lawns. Having no such fortifications, we retreated to the brick pillars of our homes. During the retreat a broken milk bottle caught me behind the ear, opening a deep gash which bled profusely. The sight of blood pouring over my face completely demoralized our ranks. My fellow-combatants left me standing paralyzed in the center of the yard, and scurried for their homes. A kind neighbor saw me and rushed me to a doctor, who took three stitches in my neck.

I sat brooding on my front steps, nursing my wound and waiting for my mother to come from work. I felt that a grave injustice had been done me. It was all right to throw cinders. The greatest harm a cinder could do was leave a bruise. But broken bottles were dangerous; they left you cut, bleeding, and helpless.

When night fell, my mother came from the white folks' kitchen. I raced down the street to meet her. I could just feel in my bones that she would understand. I knew she would tell me exactly what to do next time. I grabbed her hand and babbled out the whole story. She examined my wound, then slapped me.

"How come yuh didn't hide?" she asked me. "How come yuh awways fightin'?"

I was outraged, and bawled. Between sobs I told her that I didn't have any trees or hedges to hide behind. There wasn't a thing I could have used as a trench. And you couldn't throw very far when you were hiding behind the brick pillars of a house. She grabbed a barrel stave, dragged me home, stripped me naked, and beat me till I had a fever of one hundred and two. She would smack my rump with the stave, and while the skin was still smarting, impart to me gems of Jim Crow wisdom. I was never to throw cinders any more. I was never to fight any more wars. I was never, never, under any conditions, to fight *white* folks again. And they were absolutely right in clouting me with the broken milk bottle. Didn't I know she was working hard every day in the hot kitchens of the white folks to make money to take care of me? When was I ever going to learn to be a good boy? She couldn't be bothered with my fights. She finished by telling me that I ought to be thankful to God as long as I lived that they didn't kill me.

All that night I was delirious and could not sleep. Each time I closed my eyes I saw monstrous white faces suspended from the ceiling, leering at me.

From that time on, the charm of my cinder yard was gone. The green trees, the trimmed hedges, the cropped lawns grew very meaningful, became a symbol. Even today when I think of white folks, the hard, sharp outlines of white houses surrounded by trees, lawns, and hedges are present somewhere in the background of my mind. Through the years they grew into an overreaching symbol of fear.

3

FROM

A Raisin in the Sun

by Lorraine Hansberry
(First produced 1959)

The black woman's learned dread of the white world and her consequent protective attitude toward both black men and children continues to infect her relationship with her family. This is, perhaps, the central conundrum in the black community, since it is a reaction to the black man's powerlessness as provider and protector, but also a primary cause of the submissive attitude that assures as powerless a position for succeeding generations.

In this selection, from an award-winning play, Lorraine Hansberry (1930–1965) dramatizes a black male's effort to overcome the timidity of both his wife and mother (who has received a large sum of money) and to pursue, in this intsance, an independent financial course. His final condemnation is, unfortunately, not unique.

(RUTH *starts serving eggs.* TRAVIS *leaps up and clasps his* FA-THER *around the middle with his legs and they face each other in mutual appreciation; slowly* WALTER *peeks around the boy to catch the ultra violent rays from his* WIFE's *eyes and draws his head back as if shot.*)

WALTER. You better get down now—and get to school, man.

TRAVIS. *(At the door.)* O.K. Good-bye. *(He exits.)*

WALTER. *(After him, pointing with pride.)* That's *my* boy. *(She looks at him in disgust and turns back to her work.)*

You know what I was thinking 'bout in the bathroom this morning?

RUTH. No.

WALTER. How come you always try to be so pleasant!

RUTH. What is there to be pleasant 'bout!

WALTER. You want to know what I was thinking 'bout in the bathroom or not!

RUTH. I know what you was thinking 'bout.

WALTER. *(Ignoring her.)* 'Bout what me and Willy Harris was talking about last night.

RUTH. *(Immediately—a refrain.)* Willy Harris is a good-for-nothing loud mouth.

WALTER. Anybody who talks to me has got to be a good-for-nothing loud mouth, ain't he? And what you know about who is just a good-for-nothing loud mouth? Charlie Atkins was just a "good-for-nothing loud mouth" too, wasn't he! When he wanted me to go in the dry-cleaning business with him. And now—he's grossing a hundred thousand a year. A hundred thousand dollars a year! You still call *him* a loud mouth!

RUTH. *(Bitterly.)* Oh, Walter Lee . . . *(She folds her head on her arms over on the table.)*

WALTER. *(Rising and coming to her and standing over her.)* You tired, ain't you? Tired of everything. Me, the boy, the way we live—this beat up hole—everything. Ain't you? *(She doesn't look up, doesn't answer.)* So tired—moaning and groaning all the time but you wouldn't do nothing to help, would you? You couldn't be on my side that long for nothing, could you?

RUTH. Walter, please leave me alone.

WALTER. A man needs for a woman to back him up . . .

RUTH. Walter—

WALTER. Mama would listen to you. You know she listen to you more than she do me and Bennie. She thinks more of you. All you have to do is just sit down with her when you was drinking your coffee one morning and talking 'bout things like you do and—*(He sits down beside her and demonstrates graphically what he thinks her methods and tone should be)*—you just sip your coffee, see, and say easy like that you been thinking 'bout that deal Walter Lee is so interested in, 'bout the store and all, and sip some more coffee, like what you saying ain't really that important to you— And the next thing you know, she be listening good and asking questions and when I come home—I can tell her the details. This ain't no fly-by-night proposition, baby. I mean we figured it out, me and Willy and Bobo.

RUTH. *(With a frown.)* Bobo?

WALTER. Yeah. You see, this little liquor store we got in mind cost seventy-five thousand and we figured the initial investment on the place be 'bout thirty thousand, see. That be ten thousand each. Course, there's a couple of hundred you got to pay so's you don't spend your life just waiting for them clowns to let your license get approved—

RUTH. You mean graft?

WALTER. *(Frowning impatiently.)* Don't call it that. See there, that just goes to show you what women understand about the world. Baby, don't *nothing* happen for you in this world 'less you pay *somebody* off!

RUTH. Walter, leave me alone! *(She raises her head and stares at him vigorously—then says, more quietly)* Eat your eggs, they gonna be cold.

WALTER. *(Straightening up from her and looking off.)* That's it. There you are. Man says to his woman: I got me a dream. His woman say: Eat your eggs. *(Sadly, but gaining in power.)* Man say: I got to take hold of this here world, baby! And a woman will say: Eat your eggs and go to work. Man say—*(Passionately now.)* Man say: I got to change my life, I'm choking to death, baby! And his woman say—*(In utter anguish as he brings his fists down on his thighs)*—Your eggs is getting cold!

RUTH. *(Softly.)* Walter, that ain't none of our money.

WALTER. *(Not listening at all or even looking at her.)* This

morning, I was lookin' in the mirror and thinking about
it . . . I'm thirty-five years old; I been married eleven years
and I got a boy who sleeps in the living-room—*(Very, very
quietly)*—and all I got nothing to give him is stories about
how rich white people live . . .

RUTH. Eat your eggs, Walter.

WALTER. DAMN MY EGGS . . . DAMN ALL THE EGGS THAT EVER
WAS!

RUTH. Then go to work.

WALTER. *(Looking up at her.)* See—I'm trying to talk to you
'bout myself—*(Shaking his head with the repetition)*—and
all you can say is eat them eggs and go to work.

RUTH. *(Wearily.)* Honey, you never say nothing new. I listen
to you every day—every night and every morning and you
never say nothing new. *(Shrugging.)* So you would rather
be Mr. Arnold than be his chauffeur. So—I would *rather*
be living in Buckingham Palace.

WALTER. That is just what is wrong with the colored women
in this world . . . Don't understand about building their
men up and making 'em feel like they somebody. Like they
can do something.

RUTH. *(Drily, but to hurt.)* There *are* colored men who do
things.

WALTER. No thanks to the colored woman.

RUTH. Well, being a colored woman I guess I can't help myself none. *(She rises and gets the ironing board and sets it
up and attacks a huge pile of rough dried clothes, sprin-
kling them in preparation for the ironing and then rolling
them into tight fat balls.)*

WALTER. *(Mumbling.)* We one group of men tied to a race of
women with small minds.

4

FROM
The Flagellants

by Carlene Hatcher Polite
(First published 1967)

The consequences of the black woman's protective, matriarchal relationship toward her family is most vividly seen in the tension created between herself and her man. From this issues the black male's adaptive attempt to bolster his image in such pursuits as adulterous affairs and gambling; moreover, as previously suggested, the higher rate of desertion and broken homes among black families can be attributed in part to the black woman's preeminence and the male's inferior position.

In the following selection, from Miss Polite's widely acclaimed novel, a black man, Jimson, recounts the historical circumstances of the trap in which he and his lover, Ideal, are caught. In the process, he suggests the black male's confused, but tangible, rancor.

". . . DON'T push me into telling you of yourself. You are the personification, the effete symbol of the enduring black matriarch. You are a holdover from slavery, the privileged nonentity who was allowed free run of Miss Ann's house to dispense domestic order as you saw fit, suckle her children, give them home-training, the benefits of your orally transmitted motherwit. You were your family's provider—warm, clean, fed. Your men were devaluated, reduced to eunuchs; although some of them could have surpassed you in running Miss Ann's house. It was you, however, who made the initial, lasting impression upon Mr. Man . . . humming folkloric guilt-inducing blues undertoned with forbidden sexuality. Escaping together to freedom, though, more often with you in the foreground; you and your man sneaked away concealed under your mammy-made skirts. If this did not earn us the legality of being 'freed slaves,' we commemorated eighteen sixty-three among ourselves, our patience-practicing selves, back of the big house, vowing to change our fates—now that Mr. Abe had sprouted the Union-saving halo. You sat reigning majestically, stuffed with house vittles, growing toward an obesity visually accentuating your picture of power.

"Up North, you again had the upper hand. You simply washed and starched your apron and applied for steady work; while your man, your brothers, your sons, sporadically worked. Domestic talents have never ceased to be in demand. Euphemistically, you can be named housekeeper, my woman, Mammy, any name that please you for what, objectively, is nothing but a slave. In spite of cooking Miss Ann's daily meals with your bare, black hands, sticking your black titty down her sons' and daughters' throats, giving wise counsel, extricating them from feeling contemptuous of their fathers, you went further and gave away your force in the name of God's will—Jesus' name. Like any slave, you hated, despised, envied them with a vengeance. Love was worked out of you. God is love . . . You were left impotent.

"At home you played both your role and all the stock gestures and attitudes you could remember of Miss Ann's. Kicking your man around, you spit upon him for not making you a Miss Ann, taught your children to be patterns of hers. If your man were fortunate, he found work suited to a jackass; but if he were at all sensitive and intelligent, quietly rebelling and suffering from the exaggerated forces of two worlds, you beat him down, castrated him. He had to be kept down in order to keep you feeling worthy, important. Do not misunderstand me; colored men are just as proud, respectful, appreciative of their matriarchal mothers as you are. We have survived and have been recipients of their strength, sweat, love, travail. However, Ideal, that is your historic past. This is now. Are you too stupid to create your eminence in a more rational, contemporary manner? Although you are educated, intelligent, some of you black bitches cannot overcome the stamp of matriarchy. You are perceptive to recognize that it is not my fault. Why cannot you help to vindicate, uplift us?

"Bury white him, blast him, blacklist him—not us. Having grown up in the matriarchy, you desire through your emotional needs to construct a patriarchy, romantically, but never actually. You realize this is a man's world and whatever the color, woman is subjected to being man's slave. Society has constructed the law this way—not I . . . Ideal, you ever wonder why you refuse to overcome castrating a man and choose only those you are able to despise? First of all, as a woman, and secondly by being a black woman in the occidental world, you have a twofold need to assert yourself. Easily I identify with your frustrations, which are not wrong, Ideal, but human.

"Black women grow up imitating their most dynamic daily influence—their mothers. She loved you, birthed you, understood, forgave you unconditionally, if she were endowed with maternity . . . Father was he from whom, naturally, you also wished to receive these attentions. The poor man, though, was out from sunup to sundown trying to eke out bread and shelter. When he returned, he sought distance, rest, no conflicts, affectionate but sleepy children. If he were a perceptive black man, he returned with the same wants coupled with the agonizing futility of his endeavors. Until his dying day, he would slave. Through his inhibited appraisals, he associated retardation with his family since he, too, could love only master. If he were free, responsible to himself alone, he would not take that crap for a moment. He did, though. That he did not fawn over you, rationalizing your every fault, but instead chose to set standards of hard-earned, far-reaching achievements thwarted your childish ego—sent you running to mother to gloss over those weaknesses which fatigued father objected to, corrected, and chastised. When mother berated him, denounced him for you publicly, you slept peacefully. However, it was still his mute sanction you desired to hear voiced. Can you not see it plainly, Ideal?

"Women replace unrelenting fathers with giants. You seek through him father plus all that father is not. You unwittingly chase men that reek of him; blindly you go off with them to find love, hoping that they will be, at once, giant and the father substitute. If he falls short of your superman standard, and is the same or less than father, you want to beat him to death, castrate him. To accomplish this end, you conjure up the defunct matriarch's role. The irony is that as you destroy him, you destroy yourself. You become morbidly incapacitated, imperturbable to your giant; even if he were to come calling, throwing himself upon your lap, begging you to see yourself as giantess. Aw, you fool . . . When will we let go the incestuous whirligig? I was expelled another time from school for writing as my 'What I Did for Summer Vacation' composition—a paper confessing my summer-long desire to penetrate my mother."

5

FROM

Manchild in the Promised Land

by Claude Brown
(First published 1965)

*Another result of the black woman's unwitting complicity
in the black man's emasculation is that many black men have
unconsciously directed their antipathy toward the most accessible target—not white racism, but the black woman herself. In the following selection taken from his autobiography,
Claude Brown suggests the depth of the black male's antipathy
toward the black woman's role in her community.*

THE WOMEN, with their votes, just ran the community.
They'd elect the councilmen. They'd elect our same old light,
bright, damn-near-white Congressman who was always making those pretty promises that never amounted to anything,
those bullshit promises. He was going to keep on doing this,
and we knew it even though we were young and high. We
could stand around and talk this shit, and we knew we were
right, because just about the only people who could vote were
the women. So this light, bright, damn-near-white and full-
of-shit cat was going to be in there just as long as women had
most of the vote. As Johnny D. once said, a woman's brain is
between her legs, and some pretty nigger who was suave, like
our good Congressman, could get up there and say, "Look,
baby, I'm going to do this and that for you." The women
would go right out and vote for him, because the nigger was
too pretty for them not to. We kept on getting the same treatment because the women were running Harlem.

Most of the people didn't know it, and this was one of the great truths that we discovered. When you got high, you'd discover a whole lot of answers to many questions. This was one of them. We knew that the women were running Harlem. The women didn't know it themselves, but we knew it. Anyway, we knew it when we got high.

We'd get high, and we'd solve all the problems of Harlem. When it wore off, we would just have to live with them all over again.

6

FROM

I Know Why the Caged Bird Sings

by Maya Angelou
(First published 1969)

*The black woman's usurpation of facets of the male's role is
partially explained by society's denial of her own femininity.
The most obvious of these is related to mainstream America's
pale, blond, blue-eyed standard of beauty. From that Western-
oriented looking-glass, the reflection most black women received of themselves was always negative, but often if they
turned to their own people, they were just as readily disap-
pointed. Those with yellow and brown complexions, being
closer to the Western image, were acceptable, but the black
or plain girl could not escape acknowledgment of her home-
liness. The damage inflicted by this concept of self touched
the very basis of a woman's identity—her femininity—and the
resultant self-doubt has plagued many black women throughout their lives.*

  *In the following autobiographical selection, Maya Angelou
vividly portrays a sixteen-year-old black girl's discovery that,
indeed, America provided her no identity. This compounded
the doubt and conflict that every adolescent faces as she grows
into womanhood.*

The Well of Loneliness was my introduction to lesbianism
and what I thought of as pornography. For months the book
was both a treat and a threat. It allowed me to see a little of

the mysterious world of the pervert. It stimulated my libido and I told myself that it was educational because it informed me of the difficulties in the secret world of the pervert. I was certain that I didn't know any perverts. Of course I ruled out the jolly sissies who sometimes stayed at our house and cooked whopping eight-course dinners while the perspiration made paths down their made-up faces. Since everyone accepted them, and more particularly since they accepted themselves, I knew that their laughter was real and that their lives were cheerful comedies, interrupted only by costume changes and freshening of make-up.

But true freaks, the "women lovers," captured yet strained my imagination. They were, according to the book, disowned by their families, snubbed by their friends and ostracized from every society. This bitter punishment was inflicted upon them because of a physical condition over which they had no control.

After my third reading of *The Well of Loneliness* I became a bleeding heart for the downtrodden misunderstood lesbians. I thought "lesbian" was synonymous with hermaphrodite, and when I wasn't actively aching over their pitiful state, I was wondering how they managed simpler body functions. Did they have a choice of organs to use, and if so, did they alternate or play favorite? Or I tried to imagine how two hermaphrodites made love, and the more I pondered the more confused I became. It seemed that having two of everything other people had, and four where ordinary people just had two, would complicate matters to the point of giving up the idea of making love at all.

It was during this reflective time that I noticed how heavy my own voice had become. It droned and drummed two or three whole tones lower than my schoolmates' voices. My hands and feet were also far from being feminine and dainty. In front of the mirror I detachedly examined my body. For a sixteen-year-old my breasts were sadly undeveloped. They could only be called skin swellings, even by the kindest critic.

The line from my rib cage to my knees fell straight without even a ridge to disturb its direction. Younger girls than I boasted of having to shave under their arms, but my armpits were as smooth as my face. There was also a mysterious growth developing on my body that defied explanation. It looked totally useless.

Then the question began to live under my blankets: How did lesbianism begin? What were the symptoms? The public library gave information on the finished lesbian—and that woefully sketchy—but on the growth of a lesbian, there was nothing. I did discover that the difference between hermaphrodites and lesbians was that hermaphrodites were "born that way." It was impossible to determine whether lesbians budded gradually, or burst into being with a suddenness that dismayed them as much as it repelled society.

I had gnawed into the unsatisfying books and into my own unstocked mind without finding a morsel of peace or understanding. And meantime, my voice refused to stay up in the higher registers where I consciously pitched it, and I had to buy my shoes in the "old lady's comfort" section of the shoe stores.

I asked Mother.

Daddy Clidell was at the club one evening, so I sat down on the side of Mother's bed. As usual she woke completely and at once. (There is never any yawning or stretching with Vivian Baxter. She's either awake or asleep.)

"Mother, I've got to talk to you . . ." It was going to kill me to have to ask her, for in the asking wouldn't it be possible that suspicion would fall on my own normality? I knew her well enough to know that if I committed almost any crime and told her the truth about it she not only wouldn't disown me but would give me her protection. But just suppose I was developing into a lesbian, how would she react? And then there was Bailey* to worry about too.

* Maya's brother.

"Ask me, and pass me a cigarette." Her calmness didn't fool me for a minute. She used to say that her secret to life was that she "hoped for the best, was prepared for the worst, so anything in between didn't come as a surprise." That was all well and good for most things but if her only daughter was developing into a . . .

She moved over and patted the bed, "Come on, baby, get in the bed. You'll freeze before you get your question out."

It was better to remain where I was for the time being.

"Mother . . . my pocketbook . . ."

"Ritie, do you mean your vagina? Don't use those Southern terms. There's nothing wrong with the word 'vagina.' It's a clinical description. Now, what's wrong with it?"

The smoke collected under the bed lamp, then floated out to be free in the room. I was deathly sorry that I had begun to ask her anything.

"Well? . . . Well? Have you got crabs?"

Since I didn't know what they were, that puzzled me. I thought I might have them and it wouldn't go well for my side if I said I didn't. On the other hand, I just might not have them, and suppose I lied and said I did?

"I don't know, Mother."

"Do you itch? Does your vagina itch?" She leaned on one elbow and jabbed out her cigarette.

"No, Mother."

"Then you don't have crabs. If you had them, you'd tell the world."

I wasn't sorry or glad not to have them, but made a mental note to look up "crabs" in the library on my next trip.

She looked at me closely, and only a person who knew her face well could have perceived the muscles relaxing and interpreted this as an indication of concern.

"You don't have a venereal disease, do you?"

The question wasn't asked seriously, but knowing Mother I was shocked at the idea. "Why, Mother, of course not.

That's a terrible question." I was ready to go back to my room and wrestle alone with my worries.

"Sit down, Ritie. Pass me another cigarette." For a second it looked as if she was thinking about laughing. That would really do it. If she laughed, I'd never tell her anything else. Her laughter would make it easier to accept my social isolation and human freakishness. But she wasn't even smiling. Just slowly pulling in the smoke and holding it in puffed cheeks before blowing it out.

"Mother, something is growing on my vagina."

There, it was out. I'd soon know whether I was to be her ex-daughter or if she'd put me in hospital for an operation.

"Where on your vagina, Marguerite?"

Uh-huh. It was bad all right. Not "Ritie" or "Maya" or "Baby." "Marguerite."

"On both sides. Inside." I couldn't add that they were fleshy skin flaps that had been growing for months down there. She'd have to pull that out of me.

"Ritie, go get me that big *Webster's* and then bring me a bottle of beer."

Suddenly, it wasn't all that serious. I was "Ritie" again, and she just asked for beer. If it had been as awful as I anticipated, she'd have ordered Scotch and water. I took her the huge dictionary that she had bought as a birthday gift for Daddy Clidell and laid it on the bed. The weight forced a side of the mattress down and Mother twisted her bed lamp to beam down on the book.

When I returned from the kitchen and poured her beer, as she had taught Bailey and me beer should be poured, she patted the bed.

"Sit down, baby. Read this." Her fingers guided my eyes to VULVA. I began to read. She said, "Read it out loud."

It was all very clear and normal-sounding. She drank the beer as I read, and when I had finished she explained it in every-day terms. My relief melted the fears and they liquidly stole down my face.

Mother shot up and put her arms around me.

"There's nothing to worry about, baby. It happens to every woman. It's just human nature."

It was all right then to unburden my heavy, heavy heart. I cried into the crook of my arm. "I thought maybe I was turning into a lesbian."

Her patting of my shoulder slowed to a still and she leaned away from me.

"A lesbian? Where the hell did you get that idea?"

"Those things growing on my . . . vagina, and my voice is too deep and my feet are big, and I have no hips or breasts or anything. And my legs are so skinny."

Then she did laugh. I knew immediately that she wasn't laughing at me. Or rather that she was laughing at me, but it was something about me that pleased her. The laugh choked a little on the smoke in its way, but finally broke through cleanly. I had to give a small laugh too, although I wasn't tickled at all. But it's mean to watch someone enjoy something and not show your understanding of their enjoyment.

When she finished with the laughter, she laid it down a peal at a time and turned to me, wiping her eyes.

"I made arrangements, a long time ago, to have a boy and a girl. Bailey is my boy and you are my girl. The Man upstairs. He don't make mistakes. He gave you to me to be my girl and that's just what you are. Now, go wash your face, have a glass of milk and go back to bed."

I did as she said but I soon discovered my new assurance wasn't large enough to fill the gap left by my old uneasiness. It rattled around in my mind like a dime in a tin cup. I hoarded it preciously, but less than two weeks later it became totally worthless.

A classmate of mine, whose mother had rooms for herself and her daughter in a ladies' residence, had stayed out beyond closing time. She telephoned me to ask if she could sleep at my house. Mother gave her permission, providing my friend telephoned her mother from our house.

When she arrived, I got out of bed and we went to the upstairs kitchen to make hot chocolate. In my room we shared mean gossip about our friends, giggled over boys and whined about school and the tedium of life. The unusualness of having someone sleep in my bed (I'd never slept with anyone except my grandmothers) and the frivolous laughter in the middle of the night made me forget simple courtesies. My friend had to remind me that she had nothing to sleep in. I gave her one of my gowns, and without curiosity or interest I watched her pull off her clothes. At none of the early stages of undressing was I in the least conscious of her body. And then suddenly, for the briefest eye span, I saw her breasts. I was stunned.

They were shaped like light-brown falsies in the five-and-ten-cent store, but they were real. They made all the nude paintings I had seen in museums come to life. In a word they were beautiful. A universe divided what she had from what I had. She was a woman.

My gown was too snug for her and much too long, and when she wanted to laugh at her ridiculous image I found that humor had left me without a promise to return.

Had I been older I might have thought that I was moved by both an esthetic sense of beauty and the pure emotion of envy. But those possibilities did not occur to me when I needed them. All I knew was that I had been moved by look-ing at a woman's breasts. So all the calm and casual words of Mother's explanation a few weeks earlier and the clinical terms of Noah Webster did not alter the fact that in a fun-damental way there was something queer about me.

I somersaulted deeper into my snuggery of misery. After a thorough self-examination, in the light of all I had read and heard about dykes and bulldaggers, I reasoned that I had none of the obvious traits—I didn't wear trousers, or have big shoulders or go in for sports, or walk like a man or even want to touch a woman. I wanted to be a woman, but that seemed to me to be a world to which I was to be eternally refused entrance.

What I needed was a boyfriend. A boyfriend would clarify

my position to the world and, even more important, to myself. A boyfriend's acceptance of me would guide me into that strange and exotic land of frills and femininity.

Among my associates, there were no takers. Understandably the boys of my age and social group were captivated by the yellow- or light-brown-skinned girls, with hairy legs and smooth little lips, and whose hair "hung down like horses' manes." And even those sought-after girls were asked to "give it up or tell where it is." They were reminded in a popular song of the times, "If you can't smile and say yes, please don't cry and say no." If the pretties were expected to make the supreme sacrifice in order to "belong," what could the unattractive female do? She who had been skimming along on life's turning but never-changing periphery had to be ready to be a "buddy" by day and maybe by night. She was called upon to be generous only if the pretty girls were unavailable.

I believe most plain girls are virtuous because of the scarcity of opportunity to be otherwise. They shield themselves with an aura of unavailableness (for which after a time they begin to take credit) largely as a defense tactic.

In my particular case, I could not hide behind the curtain of voluntary goodness. I was being crushed by two unrelenting forces: the uneasy suspicion that I might not be a normal female and my newly awakening sexual appetite.

I decided to take matters into my own hands. (An unfortunate but apt phrase.)

Up from the hill from our house, and on the same side of the street, lived two handsome brothers. They were easily the most eligible young men in the neighborhood. If I was going to venture into sex, I saw no reason why I shouldn't make my experiment with the best of the lot. I didn't really expect to capture either brother on a permanent basis, but I thought if I could hook one temporarily I might be able to work the relationship into something more lasting.

I planned a chart for seduction with surprise as my opening ploy. One evening as I walked up the hill suffering from youth's vague malaise (there was simply nothing to do), the brother I had chosen came walking directly into my trap.

"Hello, Marguerite." He nearly passed me.

I put the plan into action. "Hey." I plunged, "Would you like to have a sexual intercourse with me?" Things were going according to the chart. His mouth hung open like a garden gate. I had the advantage and so I pressed it.

"Take me somewhere."

His response lacked dignity, but in fairness to him I admit that I had left him little chance to be suave.

He asked, "You mean, you're going to give me some trim?"

I assured him that that was exactly what I was about to give him. Even as the scene was being enacted I realized the imbalance in his values. He thought I was giving him something, and the fact of the matter was that it was my intention to take something from him. His good looks and popularity had made him so inordinately conceited that they blinded him to that possibility.

We went to a furnished room occupied by one of his friends, who understood the situation immediately and got his coat and left us alone. The seductee quickly turned off the lights. I would have preferred them left on, but didn't want to appear more aggressive than I had been already. If that was possible.

I was excited rather than nervous, and hopeful instead of frightened. I had not considered how physical an act of seduction would be. I had anticipated long soulful tongued kisses and gentle caresses. But there was no romance in the knee which forced my legs, nor in the rub of hairy skin on my chest.

Unredeemed by shared tenderness, the time was spent in laborious gropings, pullings, yankings and jerkings.

Not one word was spoken.

My partner showed that our experience had reached its climax by getting up abruptly, and my main concern was how to get home quickly. He may have sensed that he had been used, or his disinterest may have been an indication that I was less than gratifying. Neither possibility bothered me.

Outside on the street we left each other with little more than "Okay, see you around."

Thanks to Mr. Freeman nine years before, I had had no pain of entry to endure, and because of the absence of romantic involvement neither of us felt much had happened.

At home I reviewed the failure and tried to evaluate my new position. I had had a man. I had been had. I not only didn't enjoy it, but my normalcy was still a question.

What happened to the moonlight-on-the-prairie feeling? Was there something so wrong with me that I couldn't share a sensation that made poets gush out rhyme after rhyme, that made Richard Arlen brave the Arctic wastes and Veronica Lake betray the entire free world?

There seemed to be no explanation for my private infirmity, but being a product (is "victim" a better word?) of the Southern Negro upbringing, I decided that I "would understand it all better by-and-by." I went to sleep.

Three weeks later, having thought very little of the strange and strangely empty night, I found myself pregnant.

7

"Queen of the Blues"

by Gwendolyn Brooks
(First published 1945)

FROM
A Street in Bronzeville

In the black world the black woman's experience had been most evocatively characterized by the blues. For in her too often blighted hopes and unfulfilled dreams reside the essential qualities of that black art: the undiminished human spirit confronting an almost unassailable adversary, the irrational vicissitudes of racism and bigotry. In the following poem, Gwendolyn Brooks, a Pulitzer Prize-winning black poetess, illuminates the black woman's search for identity and for the black man who will love and respect her.

QUEEN OF THE BLUES

Mame was singing
At the Midnight Club.
And the place was red
With blues.
She could shake her body
Across the floor.
For what did she have
to lose?

She put her mama
Under the ground
Two years ago.
(Was it three?)
She covered that grave
With roses and tears.
(A handsome thing
To see.)

She didn't have any
Legal pa
To glare at her,
To shame
Her off the floor
Of the Midnight Club.
Poor Mame.

She didn't have any
Big brother
To shout
"No sister of mine! . ."
She didn't have any
Small brother
To think she was everything
Fine.

She didn't have any
Baby girl
With velvet
Pop-open eyes.
She didn't have any
Sonny boy
To tell sweet
Sonny boy lies.

"Show me a man
What will love me
Till I die.
Now show me a man

What will love me
Till I die.
Can't find no such a man
No matter how hard
You try.
Go 'long, baby.
Ain't a true man left
In Chi.

"I loved my daddy.
But what did my daddy
Do?
I loved my daddy.
But what did my daddy
Do?
Found him a brown-skin chicken
What's gonna be
Black and blue.

"I was good to my daddy.
Gave him all my dough.
I say, I was good to my daddy.
I gave him all of my dough.
Scrubbed hard in them white folks'
Kitchens
Till my knees was rusty
And so'."

The M.C. hollered,
"Queen of the blues!
Folks, this is strictly
The queen of the blues!"
She snapped her fingers.
She rolled her hips.
What did she have
To lose?

But a thought ran through her
Like a fire.

"Men don't tip their
Hats to me.
They pinch my arms
And they slap my thighs.
But when has a man
Tipped his hat to me?"

Queen of the blues!
Queen of the blues!
Strictly, strictly,
The queen of the blues!

Men are low down
Dirty and mean.
Why don't they tip
Their hats to a queen?

8

FROM
Black Bourgeoisie
by E. Franklin Frazier
(First published 1957)

*Until recently, the overwhelming majority of black people
have accepted the goal of integration as their foremost aim.
Consequently, they have striven to be accepted in mainstream
America—the white world. Almost universally the effort has
been futile. But as a result of the efforts of those few economically able to affect the pretense, a distinct class of Afro-
Americans has developed. These are the Brahmins among
black Americans—the black bourgeoisie.*

*In the following selection, the eminent sociologist, E.
Franklin Frazier (1894–1962), analyzes the internal functioning of the black bourgeoisie, focusing on the role of the
black woman. Frazier objectively delineates the illusions and
unfulfilled lives of black women who, while striving to avoid
identification with blacks, seek social status through emula-
tion of the white world.*

SINCE the black bourgeoisie live largely in a world of make-
believe, the masks which they wear to play their sorry roles
conceal the feelings of inferiority and of insecurity and the
frustrations that haunt their inner lives. Despite their attempt
to escape from real identification with the masses of Negroes,
they can not escape the mark of oppression any more than
their less favored kinsmen. In attempting to escape identifica-

tion with the black masses, they have developed a self-hatred that reveals itself in their deprecation of the physical and social characteristics of Negroes. Likewise, their feelings of inferiority and insecurity are revealed in their pathological struggle for status within the isolated Negro world and craving for recognition in the white world. Their escape into a world of make-believe with its sham "society" leaves them with a feeling of emptiness and futility which causes them to constantly seek an escape in new delusions. . . .

Among the women of the black bourgeoisie there is an intense fear of the competition of white women for Negro men. They often attempt to rationalize their fear by saying that the Negro man always occupies an inferior position in relation to the white woman or that he marries much below his "social" status. They come nearer to the source of their fear when they confess that there are not many eligible Negro men and that these few should marry Negro women. That such rationalizations conceal deep-seated feelings of insecurity is revealed by the fact that generally they have no objection to the marriage of white men to Negro women, especially if the white man is reputed to be wealthy. In fact, they take pride in the fact and attribute these marriages to the "peculiar" charms of Negro women. In fact, the middle-class Negro woman's fear of the competition of white women is based often upon the fact that she senses her own inadequacies and shortcomings. Her position in Negro "society" and in the larger Negro community is often due to some adventitious factor, such as a light complexion or a meager education, which has pushed her to the top of the social pyramid. The middle-class white woman not only has a white skin and straight hair, but she is generally more sophisticated and interesting because she has read more widely and has a larger view of the world. The middle-class Negro woman may make fun of the "plainness" of her white competitor and the latter's lack of "wealth" and interest in "society"; nevertheless she still feels insecure when white women appear as even potential competitors.

Both men and women among the black bourgeoisie have a feeling of insecurity because of their constant fear of the loss of status. Since they have no status in the larger American society, the intense struggle for status among middle-class Negroes is, as we have seen, an attempt to compensate for the contempt and low esteem of the whites. Great value is, therefore, placed upon all kinds of status symbols. Academic degrees, both real and honorary, are sought in order to secure status. Usually the symbols are of a material nature implying wealth and conspicuous consumption. Sometimes Negro doctors do not attend what are supposedly scientific meetings because they do not have a Cadillac or some other expensive automobile. School teachers wear mink coats and maintain homes beyond their income for fear that they may lose status. The extravagance in "social" life generally is due to an effort not to lose status. But in attempting to overcome their fear of loss of status they are often beset by new feelings of insecurity. In spite of their pretended wealth, they are aware that their incomes are insignificant and that they must struggle to maintain their mortgaged homes and the show of "wealth" in lavish "social" affairs. Moreover, they are beset by a feeling of insecurity because of their struggles to maintain a show of wealth through illegal means. From time to time "wealthy" Negro doctors are arrested for selling narcotics and performing abortions. The life of many a "wealthy" Negro doctor is shortened by the struggle to provide diamonds, minks, and an expensive home for his wife.

There is much frustration among the black bourgeoisie despite their privileged position within the segregated Negro world. Their "wealth" and "social" position can not erase the fact that they are generally segregated and rejected by the white world. Their incomes and occupations may enable them to escape the cruder manifestations of racial prejudice, but they cannot insulate themselves against the more subtle forms of racial discrimination. These discriminations cause frustrations in Negro men because they are not allowed to play the "masculine role" as defined by American culture. They cannot assert themselves or exercise power as white men do. When they protest against racial discrimination there is always the threat that they will be punished by the white world. In spite of the movement toward the wider integration of the Negro into the general stream of American life, middle-class Negroes are still threatened with the loss of positions and earning power if they insist upon their rights. After the Supreme Court of the United States ruled that segregation in public education was illegal, Negro teachers in some parts of the South were dismissed because they would not sign statements supporting racial segregation in education.

As one of the results of not being able to play the "masculine role," middle-class Negro males have tended to cultivate their "personalities" which enable them to exercise considerable influence among whites and achieve distinction in the Negro world. Among Negroes they have been noted for their glamour. In this respect they resemble women who use their "personalities" to compensate for their inferior status in relation to men. This fact would seem to support the observation of an American sociologist that the Negro was "the lady among the races," if he had restricted his observation to middle-class males among American Negroes.

In the South the middle-class Negro male is not only prevented from playing a masculine role, but generally he must let Negro women assume leadership in any show of militancy. This reacts upon his status in the home where the tradition of female dominance, which is widely established among Negroes, has tended to assign a subordinate role to the male. In fact, in middle-class families, especially if the husband has risen in social status through his own efforts and married a member of an "old" family or a "society" woman, the husband is likely to play a pitiful role. The greatest compliment that can be paid such a husband is that he "worships his wife," which means that he is her slave and supports all her extravagances and vanities. But, of course, many husbands in such positions escape from their frustrations by having extra-marital sex relations. Yet the conservative and conventional middle-class husband presents a pathetic picture. He often sits at home alone, impotent physically and socially, and complains that his wife has gone crazy about poker and "society" and constantly demands money for gambling and expenditures which he cannot afford. Sometimes he enjoys the sympathy of a son or daughter who has not become a "socialite." Such children often say that they had a happy family life until "mamma took to poker."

Preoccupation with poker on the part of the middle-class woman is often an attempt to escape from a frustrated life. Her frustration may be bound up with her unsatisfactory sexual life. She may be married to a "glamorous" male who neglects her for other women. For among the black bourgeoisie, the glamour of the male is often associated with his sexual activities. The frustration of many Negro women has a sexual origin. Even those who have sought an escape from frustration in sexual promiscuity may, because of satiety or deep psychological reasons, become obsessed with poker in order to escape from their frustrations. One "society" woman, in justification of her obsession with poker, remarked that it had taken the place of her former preoccupation with sex. Another said that to win at poker was similar to a sexual orgasm.

The frustration of the majority of the women among the black bourgeoisie is probably due to the idle or ineffectual lives which they lead. Those who do not work devote their time to the frivolities of Negro "society." When they devote their time to "charity" or worth-while causes, it is generally a form of play or striving for "social" recognition. They are constantly forming clubs which ostensibly have a serious purpose, but in reality are formed in order to consolidate their position in "society" or to provide additional occasions for playing poker. The idle, overfed women among the black bourgeoisie are generally, to use their language, "dripping with diamonds." They are forever dieting and reducing only to put on more weight (which is usually the result of the food that they consume at their club meetings). Even the women among the black bourgeoisie who work exhibit the same frustrations. Generally, they have no real interest in their work and only engage in it in order to be able to provide the conspicuous consumption demanded by "society." As we have indicated, the women as well as the men among the black bourgeoisie read very little and have no interest in music, art, or the theater. They are constantly restless and do not know how to relax. They are generally dull people and only become animated when "social" matters are discussed, especially poker games. They are afraid to be alone and constantly seek to be surrounded by their friends, who enable them to escape from their boredom.

The frustrated lives of the black bourgeoisie are reflected in the attitudes of parents towards their children. Middle-class Negro families as a whole have few children, while among the families that constitute Negro "society" there are many childless couples. One finds today, as an American observed over forty years ago, that "where the children are few, they are usually spoiled" in middle-class Negro families. There is often not only a deep devotion to their one or two children, but a subservience to them. It is not uncommon for the only son to be called and treated as the "boss" in the family. Parents cater to the transient wishes of their children and often rationalize their behavior towards them on the grounds that children should not be "inhibited." They spend large sums of money on their children for toys and especially for clothes. They provide their children with automobiles when they go to college. All of this is done in order that the children may maintain the status of the parents and be eligible to enter the "social" set in Negro colleges. When they send their children to northern "white" colleges they often spend more time in preparing them for what they imagine will be their "social" life than in preparing them for the academic requirements of these institutions.

In their fierce devotion to their children, which generally results in spoiling them, middle-class Negro parents are seemingly striving at times to establish a human relationship that will compensate for their own frustrations in the realm of human relationships. Devotion to their children often becomes the one human tie that is sincere and free from the competition and artificiality of the make-believe world in which they live. Sometimes they may project upon their children their own frustrated professional ambitions. But usually, even when they send their children to northern "white" universities as a part of their "social" striving within the Negro community, they seem to hope that their children will have an acceptance in the white world which has been denied them.

9

FROM

Silent Voices: The Southern Negro Woman Today

by Josephine Carson

(First published 1969)

Contrasted with the striving black bourgeoisie, the lower-class black woman seldom has the means or the expectations of a better life for herself. Although she may have hope for her children, her main goal is survival. In the following interview, Irene Williams, from Atlanta, Georgia, displays an intuitive wit, a stoic sense of reality, and an awareness and insight into both the black and white worlds that are not uncommon among lower-class blacks. The selection begins with Josephine Carson entering the Too Tight Barbershop in an attempt to locate a young black woman, Lucy Toomis, for an interview.

THIS neighborhood is getting to me. Today Richard, the director of the house, and I go at noon to the Too Tight Barbershop, where he gets his hair cut, to find Lucy Toomis, a young Negro woman who hangs around there picking up men.

The Too Tight is on a corner, a narrow white stucco building with an undecipherable sign on the outer wall describing some business of former years. Inside there is no light, but a general mumble and shuffle takes place as we enter; and I become aware of the presence of at least six men, all black. They move to the back of the shop, whispering. It is a two-chair shop, clean but suspiciously unindustrious in atmosphere, like a front for some questionable activity; it may be just that the lights are out. The barbershop is an ideal men's club, and this slum, like all others, no doubt, breeds an idle male population. They are everywhere and when not on the street are clustered in small stores and saloons, or in cars which are sometimes long past mobility and slump on rusty rims in back yards, side streets, and alleys.

The barber, obsequious and astonished, comes forward, blocking further passage. Although he wants not to look at me he must. He stares at Richard with very wide eyes. I must be a government woman or social worker, that is the only explanation. This is holy territory that excludes women, especially white women. Who ever heard of a white woman entering this door? I feel like apologizing to him but let Richard do the talking. I hear a conniving little laugh from somewhere in the shadows of the shop as Richard states our business. The barber is very kind.

"Lucy? She done got her a job. Workin'. Her motha down the street though. You wanta talk to her?"

"Well . . . that would be nice. You think she'd mind?"

"No'm, she don't mind. I'll git her."

He goes out in such a way as to force us to do the same. Richard leaves. I stand on the street with the barber who, with two fingers in his mouth, whistles to Lucy's mother to join us. He waves then, beckoning her. "She comin'. She be right here."

First view of Mrs. Irene Williams: A short, stocky body, lean and muscular looking, in a white uniform that strikes the lower shin just above a rumpled pair of dark boys' socks with a design up the side. The feet are thrust into sneakers without laces; the arms are partly hidden in a shapeless green sweater without elbows and without most buttons. The face, light-skinned with heavy African lips, bears an expression of stupefied horror. She is drunk, a chronic sort of drunk, immediately evident as she comes close; there is the odor of saturated, sugared alcoholic chemistry—dense, fruity, rank; no chlorophyll. The mouth is open in a kind of brutish wonder. The left eye, enduring a huge purple and yellow mottled shiner acquired about two days ago, is still swollen, the cornea streaked with fine red threads; red-ringed eyes gaze as indiscriminately as those of a staring corpse. She stumbles forward, eager to oblige. Her hair stands straight up as if magnetized into an arc of gray and black streaks three inches above the face.

"Whatsa mattah?"

"Nothin'. This lady wants to talk to ya. Here . . ." He motions me toward her as if she were an object. "She'll talk to ya." His tone is sweet, paternal toward me. I feel dreadful, hysterical. Why no protest? I have invaded; yes, this whole work is an invasion. Yes, I know that it is an invasion. *Obscene*—that is how it felt to James Agee to live with and observe innocent hosts who floundered, starved, and grappled for decency in the splintered ruin of their lives.

I thank the barber with a smile. He lowers his eyes and lunges back into the Too Tight with a grunt, and enough of Miss Ann or worse. A crescendo of laughter greets him.

"What you want, Sweetheart?" Mrs. Williams stares at me as I imagine stone age woman might do. "You from Lucy's insurance?"

"No, no." I tell her my purpose.

"Well . . . sure . . . I'll talk to ya." Incredulous. "Come on down the house. We set on the poach."

We walk down the block. "I won't take ya inside. Ain't cause you white, but my house a terrible mess today. I hasn't cleaned nothin' yet." Sneaky laugh. "I hates to go into it myse'f." I laugh with her, relieved.

We pass a row of slum houses, now and then a neat one, white perhaps or yellow, with a veranda and a few flower beds. Most, though, are abused, haggard, collapsing, almost clownishly dejected structures. There is always a stoop; it is always broken. I see windows patched with board and a rooster between houses. The rooster crows suddenly, a cracked strangled cry like the wailing of an Arab. A rooster, that most rural of creatures, incarcerated in the city slum, wails for all who share his fate. . . .

"That silly thing don't know *what* time it is," says my guide.

She waves, as we pass, to a dark elderly couple who rock solemnly on a high veranda. They do not return the salute. She may be a pariah in the neighborhood if she is drunk all the time, if the black eye was produced by a domestic row.

"Doze my neighbor. Nice folks. Here my place."

Hers is a small duplex made of composition that from a distance resembles brick. Up close it is just crude, cheap, ugly siding, probably durable. The porch floor is cement; it sags and has wide cracks but seems sturdy. Mrs. Williams blows on the seat of a rusted white metal porch chair and offers it to me. I sit; she, at my side, faces the street. She stares, her eyes stunned open. I doubt that she can close them; they seem sprung. She passes the limits of the pitiful and is almost ridiculous—yet the availability, the graciousness, and the utter immediacy of the innocent drunk share with the candor of ignorance the terrain of her long face, her square youngish jaw, and there is nothing in this face but sheer humility and gentleness for a stranger.

"I hope to find a lot of different women, all sorts, who will talk and say how they feel and what they think about the world . . ." I am telling her. It seems insane, irrelevant, but I get it out. She nods, appreciative, patient, even eager to grasp it. She talks a little—about an Alabama childhood, a big family, mother, grandmother, auntie, sister . . . It is a familiar recital.

"Hit's pritty there. My motha, she still there. Grandmotha, too. Bofe."

"You ever go home?"

"No'm, not too much. My baby in school here an' I got my husban' and he don't like to go. Don't seem to like Alabama. I don't know . . .

"My baby? Oh, she's a big girl now, ten years old. Her name Virginia. I git you a picture. Wait here. I ain't goin' to bring you in . . . 'scuse me but this house a mess today . . ." She disappears into it and comes out with two pictures; the first is of her daughter, in a small gilt frame—a tinted photo of a glowing face, all teeth and cheeks and huge radiant eyes, two braids, ribbons. One has no difficulty in exclaiming: "Oh, she's beautiful!"

"She smart, too. Make all A's and B's. That all she bring me home. A's and B's. Not like Lucy. She don't bring me nothin' but trouble. Used to be me and Lucy was close but . . ." Her voice dims. "Don't know what happen to me and Lucy. We was friends but she run off from her husban' . . . come bangin' in here with them three kids. She and me fightin' all the time now. My husban' too, he fight her."

"You all live together here?" She nods. "How many rooms?"

"We gots three. The boys have cots in de kitchen. Takes 'em out to the back poach in the mornin'."

"Oh, that's hard. How can you manage in three rooms, four kids and three adults? I'm not surprised you fight."

"Honey, it's awful. Gets me down. I get to drinkin' . . . I don't know . . . well, I drinks. I don't lie to the Lord, why'd I lie to you? I tell de truth—I drinks. It heps me."

"It must be hard on your husband, too. What does he do?"

"Oh, he . . . seem like he say he paintin' now. House painter. I don't rightly know just what he doin' now but often he'll house paint. It wear him out, these chillrun all over him. He not so young. Gits angry . . . commence to holler . . ." Her head sways slowly in wonderment, as if she is just realizing it all.

"Oh, that's too hard. Any chance Lucy might move out?"

"Well . . . it be pritty bad. She might could move sometime."

I falter, having pushed too far. I ask about Virginia's school, Reed School. Is it integrated? Richard's children are the only whites there, I have been told.

"They gots three o' fo'."

"Think they'll ever really integrate it?"

"Well, 'scuse me, Honey, but I don't want no integration in that school." The humble honest half-drunk gaze hangs on mine. "Me and you, it different. We talk. Womens is different. But I don't want no mo' whites in that school with my baby."

"Why not, Mrs. Williams?"

"Listen . . . you ever hear of the 'inferotty compless'?"

I could weep. "Yes, I know what that is."

"Well, that what goin' to happen to my baby if they brings them white chillrun in there. She bringing home A's and B's now just fine but you git them white chillruns comin' in there and she goin' to be lookin' at them all day, say: 'What they doin'? What they talkin'? What they clothes?' No *ma'am*! Scuse me, Honey, but I don't want them white chillrun in that school. Jess what they got now is plenty."

"You really think that would bother her for more than a few days?"

"I knows it."

"I've heard from other mothers, both Negro and white, that the children get along fine if the adults leave them alone."

"Well . . ." She wants very much to allow for me and my "rational" view of things, but how rational has her life been, how rational is it now? The look is patient, apologetic, firm and kind. That is character. I retreat.

"Well, maybe you're right, Mrs. Williams. I know I wouldn't want my children upset when things are going well for them in school. It's too much to ask of them, maybe."

She is relieved. She hands me the other frame, a larger one, also cheap metal, filigreed and shining. She swipes at the glass hastily with the tail of her sweater.

"This here my son, Lucy's baby brother."

I behold an adult male version of the little girl, young, heroic, innocent, beautiful, manly; a movie hero. It is a tinted sepia photo, peach-toned and glowing. The face is incredibly handsome. He wears the uniform of a high ranking military officer. Mrs. Williams' hand hovers near the frame as if to guard or even snatch it from me.

"What a handsome man! Is he still in the service?"

"Yessum. He have a job only two Negro men in the United States have, that special kinda rate he have. Only two doin' what he doin'. He graduate Morehouse College eight years ago."

"That's a great school. You must be proud of him."

"Oh, yeah. He got scholarships. Went all thoo. Graduate honor man. He live in California now, have him a wife and two babies. He all the time callin' me: 'Mama, please don't drink no mo'. Mama, come on out here to California.' He don't understand . . . you know . . . Oh, he'd send me a airplane ticket if I wants to go. He say, 'If it git too bad, Mama, you come on out here.' But I won't fly in no airplanes! I'm too scared!" She grins but the laugh is frozen in.

"You could take the train."

"Take too long. I don't know. One o' these days I'm goin', though. When it git too bad. I might could take my baby and go." The testament of the big mottled purplish sock-in-the-eye is there. "When it git too bad." When does it get too bad? From terrible to desperate—is the transition even noticeable to the brutalized? We are silent together now. She has not spoken with self-pity. I want no trace of false self-pity to be recorded here in her words; there is none. She requests nothing from me. But we sit here together in the quiet chill, in the scuff of wind among dried leaves and dust, in the abandoned air that only the frantic displaced rooster—far off, a cockeyed lament—cares to claim; we do sit here and must therefore receive one another now, in this ragged, broken place on these cold half-rusted third-hand chairs, on this runt of a porch in a slummy street; we sit here, she and I, and all at once we are bound, wound together in that lower common being of survival to which she has carefully drawn me down, so that I see no longer these mere dismal sights but below them, deeper, to a sort of grim purity; and I understand her suddenly, not knowing how it has happened. That rare, un-summoned series of revelations has taken place—that opening of doors—and she who has said, "I won't take you inside . . . ain't 'cause you white," has taken me inside. Or I have en-tered there in spite of both of us? And not because I am white or anything that I am or she is, but only because we two women talking together forgot to defend ourselves.

"When it git too bad . . ."

Someone called Irene Williams—a drunk woman on a windy street, perpetually hurled into her living, her waking and sleeping by what she cannot describe, with which she can-not cope—that someone looks at me now, decently and hon-estly, and I at her. Her eyes blur, drown quickly in tears with-out rescue. She lowers her gaze, not her head. She drowns and says, "Scuse me." And I pat her arm stupidly.

Sudden anger attacks me. Why can't she go now, today, this afternoon, on a plane to California and visit her son? Or stay there? He has the money; why doesn't he come and take her? But now, from the point of purity, I know that all that takes imagination, and hers is devoured in the process of en-during one day and then the next of self-perpetuating trou-ble. Beyond today there is nothing, and nothing is something like peace. And so we sit silently.

Later. The talk is easy, free, intimate.

About women: "You know what I think the whole trouble is? Them pants they wears. Can't tell the women from the mens no mo'. See 'em goin' by on the street and you don't know *what* it is. I tell Lucy them pants don't look good but she wear 'em.

"You got such pritty hair, Honey. That you real hair color?"

"Yes."

"Pritty. Well, the trouble with womens? Oh . . . mens, that's they biggest trouble. Now, I used to work and that were bet-

ter. My husban' don't always git work. But I got these little
chillrun of Lucy 'round here and I got Virginia, she need me
'round. But Lucy workin' now. Got her a job lass week. She
goin' to do better, I know it. I be busy. Got my housework,
cookin' . . . No'm, I don't so much like the house no mo'. The
work too hard. And it don't only git done till they got it all
tore up again.

"My neighbor? He a preacher, got him a little church
down the street. Very nice man. He hep me out one time I
have trouble with my husban'. He very quiet and nice. *Some*
colored mens is nice, Honey, you know that?

"Me, I think I'd rather talk to a woman. I b'lieve I would.
Mens, I likes 'em but not to talk." And shyly, with a kind of
grimace of friendliness, "Me and you does all right.

"Oh, yeah, I and my motha, we close. Grandmotha, too.
My daddy somewhere up north lass time we heard. I haven't
seen him since . . . oh, 'bout forty-two. Wartime. We all come
up on a farm. Alabama. It's nice ovah there."

"It seems more like home to you than Georgia?"

"Yes ma'am, it do. Alabama my true home. It the onliest
place I calls home.

"Civil Right? It comin' along. But they got mo' trouble
comin', if they don't know it. Lotsa mo' trouble.

"Gov'ner Sanders? I don't know too much about him. He
race-minded, I hear. Don't want Negroes in anywheres.

"President Johnson? He seem like a nice fella, what he
doin' for the po', but . . .

"President Kennedy? I loved him! I *loved* him! All us loved
him.

"What I knows about that Vietnam, it's a big mess. I don't
b'lieve in war, anyways. Well, my son got to make up his own
mind. If *they* goes, *he* got to go. That's how it is.

"No'm, I doesn't vote. Maybe next time. They come thoo
here wantin' me to vote. I done regiss but I haven't vote yet.
Maybe I will. I know it's important.

"Oh, yes ma'm, I believes in the Lord. I loves the Lord. Wasn't fo' the Lord . . ." She shakes her head.

"You come back ovah to see me, you hear? I be round here on the street most the days. You come back."

All that in drunkenness. She stands and waves me away, her hand stiffly open, bent-fingered, frozen halfway through a wave, a grasp at nothing; only poised in the instant.

10

"Mother to Son"

by Langston Hughes
(First published 1926)

FROM
Selected Poems

Many black women, forsaking the attention and luxuries that white middle-class mothers take for granted, overcame their problems by totally dedicating their lives to their children. In the following poem, Langston Hughes alludes to the black mother's travails and her preeminent concern with giving her son the courage to go on.

MOTHER TO SON

Well, Son, I'll tell you:
Life for me ain't been no crystal stair.
It's had tacks in it,
And splinters,
And boards torn up,
And places with no carpet on the floor—
Bare.
But all the time
I'se been a-climbin' on,
And reachin' landin's,
And turnin' corners,
And sometimes going in the dark

Where there ain't been no light.
So, boy, don't you turn back.
Don't you set down on the steps
'Cause you finds it's kinder hard.
Don't you fall now—
For I'se still goin', honey,
I'se still climbin',
And life for me ain't been no crystal stair.

11

"Granny: The Guardian of the Generations"

by E. Franklin Frazier
(First published 1939)

FROM

The Negro Family in the United States

When the black woman reaches that ultimate matriarchal role as grandmother, she often takes on a new dimension. In contrast to mainstream America's elderly, who usually spend their waning years in subsidiary or parasitic roles, the grandmother in the black family traditionally has held a commanding position. In addition to providing her offspring's families with services often furnished by babysitters and domestics in middle-class homes, she has usually acquired the role of tutelary head of her household. Although the black male's bold thrust for realization of his masculine role in recent years, and the increased numbers of black families financially able to adopt the life style and ethos of middle-class America, have lessened the importance of the grandmother in black households, she still maintains a prestigious if often tertiary position in the black community.

The following sociological selection, published thirty-one years ago, describes a role which, though somewhat diminished in importance now, continues to affect the lives of black women in their communities.

DURING the Civil War an old slave and his wife attempted to escape from a plantation near Savannah but were caught and returned to their master. While the old man was receiving five hundred lashes as punishment, his wife collected "her children and grandchildren, to the number of twenty-two, in a neighboring marsh, preparatory to another attempt that night. They found a flatboat which had been rejected as unseaworthy, got on board—still under the old woman's orders—and drifted forty miles down the river" to the lines of the Union army. An officer who was on board the gunboat that picked them up said that "when the 'flat' touched the side of the vessel, the grandmother rose to her full height with her youngest grandchild in her arms, and said only, 'My God! are we free?' " [1]

The energy, courage, and devotion of this woman, who was nearly seventy, are characteristic of the role which the grandmother played in the Negro family. During slavery the Negro grandmother occupied in many instances an important place in the plantation economy and was highly esteemed by both the slaves and the masters. In the master's house she was very often the "mammy" whom history and tradition have idealized because of her loyalty and affection. Because of her intimate relations with the whites, "all family secrets," as Calhoun observes, "were in her keeping; she was the defender of the family honor. The tie of affection between her and her charges was never outgrown. Often she was the confidential advisor of the older members of the household. To young mothers she was an authority on first babies." [2] Age added dignity to her position, and "her regime," as Thomas Nelson Page says, "extended frequently through two generations, occasionally through three." Writing of her grandmother, a former slave remarks: "She became an indispensable person

1. Thomas Wentworth Higginson, *Army Life in a Black Regiment* (New York, 1900), pp. 332-33.
2. Arthur W. Calhoun, *A Social History of the American Family* (Cleveland, 1917–18), II, p. 284.

in the household, officiating in all capacities, from cook and wet-nurse to seamstress." [3] From Frederick Douglass, who was reared by his grandmother and grandfather, we have the following testimony:

I infer that my grandmother, especially, was held in high esteem, far higher than was the lot of most colored persons in that region. She was a good nurse, and a capital hand at making nets used for catching shad and herring, and was, withal, somewhat famous as a fisherwoman, and remarkable for her success in keeping her seedling sweet potatoes through the months of winter, and easily got the reputation of being born to "good luck." In planting time Grandmother Betsy was sent for in all directions, simply to place the seedling potatoes in the hills or drills; for the superstition had it that her touch was needed to make them grow. This reputation was full of advantage to her and her grandchildren, for a good crop, after her planting for the neighbors, brought her a share of the harvest.[4]

The grandmother's prestige and importance were as great among the slaves on the plantation as among the whites in the master's house. She was the repository of the accumulated lore and superstition of the slaves and was on hand at the birth of black children as well as of white. She took under her care the orphaned and abandoned children. A former slave recalled that the usual scanty fare of slaves caused her no trouble; for, she wrote, "on my various errands I passed my grandmother's house and she always had something to spare for me. I was frequently threatened with punishment if I stopped there; and my grandmother, to avoid detaining me, often stood at the gate with something for my breakfast or dinner. I was indebted to her for all my comforts, spiritual or temporal." This same grandmother, because of her dignity and the esteem in which she was held by the community, was bought and emancipated by a kindly old woman. This was done when, at the death of her mistress, she forestalled an at-

3. L. Maria Child, *The Freedmen's Book* (Boston, 1865), pp. 206-07.
4. *Life and Times of Frederick Douglass* (Chicago, 1882), p. 14.

tempt to sell her privately to a trader by insisting upon mounting the public auction block with the other slaves. Later she gathered under her care two generations of her descendants.

When emancipation came, it was often the old grandmother who kept the generations together. One who worked with the newly emancipated slaves during and after the Civil War has left us a picture of one of these old women presiding over four generations of descendants. Miss Botume writes concerning Tamar, a robust, merry-looking, middle-aged woman:

Her mother and grandmother lived in the room with her. She also had three children, one of whom was married and lived there with his wife and baby, which baby the oldest woman was "minding."

It was something to see five generations together, all apparently in good condition. At my request, Ned, the young father, took the baby, and all stood in a row. In the old vernacular they would have been called "a prime lot of niggers." I never saw a more fearless and self-contained set. They were all very black, and had been considered valuable, and they knew their own importance.[5]

The sentiments and feelings that lay beneath the quiet dignity and force of these old women are only dimly reflected in the recorded observations of those who knew them in the past. But occasionally we run across a former slave on one of the plantations of the South who forms a link between the past and the present. A grandmother who was a former slave living on a small plot of land that was once a part of a large plantation in Alabama told the following story:

I was 77 years old this last gone February. I satisfied I'm oldern that, but that's what the white folks gied me when I was freed, but if I don't disremember, that's my sister's age. When war was declared and freedom come, I was nursing and working at the white folks house. They jest got us niggers all mixed up. I re-

5. Elizabeth Hyde Botume, *First Days among the Contrabands* (Boston, 1893), p. 56.

206 TO BE A BLACK WOMAN: PORTRAITS IN FACT AND FICTION

members well when the people was drilling ter free the slaves.
That's why I knows I'm oldern that. I ain't got naire child but
one son up in Ohio and he ain't a bit a use ter me. Hits hurtin'
too ter raise chillen grown and they don't care 'bout you. I been
married twice. I had one child by my first husband. That's my son
in Ohio I was tellin' you 'bout. I had three chillen by my second
husband and they all dead 'cept one, that's him. My husband
been dead now going on three years. I got one grandchild but hit
ain't wid me. The two little orphan chillen I raised, they here
wid me. I got four acres of land, me and the chillen. I let them
work out fer people so they will come and plow fer us. This my
own little house and four acres he left me on. My husband said he
wanted his own house. I pays $3.10 fer taxes ever year. Last year,
I didn't make naire bale of cotton. Hit wont a half bale. See I
hafta 'vide my little land up wid cotton, corn and 'taters. I jest
make 'nough ter barely pay my taxes. These little orphan chillen
mother dead and father dead too. I'm they great aunt. Me being
the oldest one and me being they mother's auntie and the oldest
head, that's how I come by them. So me and my husband raised
them chillen from leetle bit a things. Sometimes I don't git food,
go widout eating all day so's ter leave hit fer them ter eat 'cause
they hafta work. I been had them in school, though I has a tough
time I send them.

In her explanation of why the responsibility for the care of
"her chillen" falls upon her, this old woman expresses the
characteristic attitude of the grandmother in her role as "oldest head" in the family. Where the maternal family organization assumes such importance as among a large section of the
Negro population, the oldest woman is regarded as the head
of the family. Some of these grandmothers will tell you of
their courting, which sounds very much like that of their
granddaughters' today. Often, instead of having been a pre-
lude to marriage, it culminated in motherhood and the responsibilities which it imposed. Even when they married,
sometimes marriage was of short duration, and the responsibility of rearing and supporting their children fell upon them.
Thus it has been the grandmother who has held the genera-

tions together when fathers and even mothers abandoned their offspring.

Although one old grandmother, whose mother, a centenarian, had just died, announced, "all my chillen done married off," two grandchildren and two daughters who worked part of the time in Montgomery were looking to her for support. With the aid of her son who lived over the hill she was working a plot of land, "not quite a one-horse farm," that was once a part of a large plantation. This old woman boasted that she had been on the place forty years and on the spot thirty years. She was the mother of fifteen children, six of whom were living. In recounting her numerous miscarriages and dead children, she said: "Some come live but didn't live no time, yet three got to be big chillen walkin' 'bout befo' dey dies. One boy got to be eighteen years old. He had dat fever and from dat, spasms and spells, and from spells he fell in de fire and got burnt and never did git over hit. De other two just died with de fever." Of her six surviving children, two were by her husband from whom she separated when she found him unsuitable to work with and four by a man to whom she had never been married. One son, who was living in Montgomery when he was drafted for the war, had not been heard from for years. This son had given his illegitimate child to his mother when it was three years old. She was also taking care of her daughter's child. This daughter, who had been deserted by her husband, was working in domestic service in Montgomery with her sister. Both sisters returned to their mother and looked for support from the land when they could no longer make a living in the city. The old grandmother, who had been ill for years, had denied herself medicine and even the consolation that when she "lay down and die" there would be "something to bury" her, in order that her grandchildren might have clothes and tuition for school. As she labored on her little plot of land, she could always renew her courage and faith by glancing at a nearby dead tree that marked her praying-ground. It was, as she said, "by dat dead tree where de Lord convert my soul at nine o'clock on a Thursday. I was over dere praying; over by dat tree was my praying-ground. I know when de Lord poured his Holy Ghost around my soul. . . . He told me to go in all parts of the world and tell what he have done for my soul."

On another "one-horse farm," for which she was paying four hundred pounds of lint cotton, a great-grandmother, who was two years and six months old when "Freedom 'clared," was living with her daughter's two grandchildren, one two years old and the other three and a half. Her daughter, who had gone to town to work as a cook and a laundress for a white family, sent something occasionally for her grandchildren. The old great-grandmother remarked concerning her granddaughter, the mother of the two children, "she ain't had ne'er a husband; dese chillen was her 'dopted chillen." The latter part of this statement turned out to mean that they, like their mother, were illegitimate. The old woman had given birth to eleven children, nine of whom were dead. Of the nine children, one was born dead; the oldest died from a fall in Montgomery; her youngest died of worms; while the others died when they were "little bits of things." Her surviving son, she said, had always been thickheaded, and, although he reached the second grade in school, he had never learned anything. With "a piece of a plow" she was making a living for herself and her great-grandchildren, the youngest of whom had a piece of copper hung about his neck to help "his teething." She had to depend upon her own efforts as she had been "kinda separated" from her second husband for two or three years. Her only consolation was that nearly a half-century ago she was converted. "I never felt," she said, "such a feeling in my life. Wouldn't go back to a life of sin for anything. Give me Jesus, if I didn't have a rag, or crumb. God got my soul." As she talked, she began to cry and added despairingly, "I'se had a hard time. Sometimes I feel like I wish I'd never been born. Jest like I travel the path of this world, may the Lord spare me to have something to eat this fall."

The Negro grandmother's importance is due to the fact not only that she has been the "oldest head" in a maternal family organization but also to her position as "granny" or midwife among a simple peasant folk. As the repository of folk wisdom concerning the inscrutable ways of nature, the grandmother has been depended upon by mothers to ease the pains of childbirth and ward off the dangers of ill luck. Children acknowledge their indebtedness to her for assuring them, during the crisis of birth, a safe entrance into the world. Even grown men and women refer to her as a second mother and sometimes show the same deference and respect for her that they accord their own mothers. In spite of the advent of the doctor, who represents the invasion of science and the rational order of civilization in the South, the "granny" is still the dependable figure who presides at the crisis of childbirth. In 1942 in rural Tennessee, 37.6 per cent of Negro live births were attended by midwives; whereas during the same year in Mississippi midwives attended four-fifths of all Negro births. In some places we can see the transition from the "granny" to the doctor. As one woman remarked: "I had a midwife but got a doctor to get the afterbirth." Although custom and tradition are largely responsible for the continued use of the midwife, the expense of securing a doctor is prohibitive for the majority of these economically dependent folk.

We have the following picture from the Sea Islands of one of these grandmothers who, after becoming too old to act as midwife, has resumed her traditional role as guardian of the younger generation:

She is seventy-four and no longer able to pursue her profession as midwife, or to engage in active work in the field. From time to time she shoulders her heavy hoe and ties up her hips with heavy cord to "gib stren'th" and does what she can. Through the migration of her daughter to Savannah, she had acquired four grandchildren to care for. The children are able to do some light work in the gathering of compost and cultivation of the crops, but there is no one to do the heavy plowing or hoeing. The land is unfenced so that the animals have to be staked out to forage and constantly watched. All of the children are visibly under-nourished and it was quite an experiment at the headquarters of the study to try to fill them up with food and to see how much would be required. Incredible quantities were eaten. When she was asked in the early spring what she had on hand in way of food she said, "Few peas and some cracked corn." [6]

So far we have seen the grandmother in her role as the head of the maternal family among a primitive peasant people. She has often played a similar important role in families, maternal in organization, which have originated through the relations of white men and colored women. In the following excerpt from the family history of a young woman in a secretarial po-sition in Chicago, we see how one grandmother is placed at the head of the family line while the other has played the usual role of looking after her daughter's mulatto child:

My maternal grandmother was a house-servant in a family in the northern part of Alabama at the time of the Civil War. This family owned a large plantation. My grandmother told me that she was a favorite in the house and had her way pretty much. During the third year of the Civil War my mother was born. Her father was the master of the house. My mother has always been very sensitive about her birth and has never wanted to talk about it before her children. When very small my mother was separated from her mother as the latter went to Tennessee because of the activities of the Ku Klux Klan. My mother was reared by her grandmother during the absence of her mother. When my grand-mother returned from Tennessee she married a minister and had three sons by this marriage. My mother spent her childhood with the family on a farm in Madison County, Alabama. She helped to care for her three half brothers.

A mulatto dentist in a northern city, who remarked con-cerning his grandmother, "My grandmother always told me something that always impressed me—that no one in the fam-ily was ever convicted of a crime," was only able to trace his

6. T. J. Woofter, Jr., *Black Yeomanry* (New York, 1930), p. 91.

family back to the Revolutionary War period because of this grandmother's recollections of her own grandmother. Continuity in this family had been maintained through the female line, since the male progenitors had been white for the first two generations and died at an early age during the next two generations. The first grandmother, according to the traditions which have come down through four generations, was a free woman of color, with a considerable mixture of Scotch blood, and lived in Baltimore. She was "seven years old when the Revolutionary War started and fourteen years old when it ended," so runs the tradition. While a bonded servant for seven years, she was kidnapped, sold as a slave, and taken to Georgia. She became the mother of a child by one of the young men in her master's family just before he left home to study at Oxford. The mulatto child was reared in the house and, when grown, was placed in charge of the domestic affairs of the household. Following the example of her mother, she had a child, who was born in 1832, by a white man. This child, who was the grandmother of the dentist, remained a dominant figure in the family until her death at ninety-six years of age. Although she was married twice during slavery, the deaths of her husbands placed upon her the responsibility of rearing the children. Through her efforts her children were sent to the schools that were established for the freedmen shortly after the Civil War and were thus started on the way to culture and achievement. Similarly we find a prominent physician's mulatto wife, whose mother objected to her being reared as white by her white father, briefly tracing her family through a number of female ancestors who had children by white men. "My great-grandmother was the offspring of a white man and an Indian squaw. She had a child, who was my grandmother, by a Negro. My grandmother had two sets of children: one by a white man, and another by a Negro. My mother was one of the children by a white father." The old great-grandmother was the real head of the family. She gathered up her descendants in Kentucky and took them to the West, where, after keeping a boardinghouse for miners, she acquired money herself through investments in the mines. Later she bought homes for her children and grandchildren and sent several of them to college.

Some of the younger generation of mixed blood give the same testimony concerning their grandmothers' dominating influence in family relations. A mulatto college student, whose grandmother lived apart from her husband after attempting unsuccessfully to "subordinate him," thought that she typified the spirit of the C—— women "who have always demanded and asserted their rights, whatever may be the costs." The mother of this girl had left her husband in the South because he was apologetic when a white man struck her. This student wrote concerning her maternal grandmother:

My favorite ancestor was my Grandma Ann. I can probably attribute this attachment to the fact that my sisters who knew her have remarked how like her I was in feature, and even tastes. I remember when as a child I would ask my mother some of the things her mother used to do when she was a little girl, and then try to do some of them myself, in an effort to be as much like her as possible. I have a very definite mental image of what I imagine she must have been like, but I can best describe her by quoting directly from my sister. "Grandma Ann—well now there was a character. Her mother must have been a clever woman to have named her so aptly. She, too, was trained as a special maid to her mistress. She sewed and did beautiful embroidery work. Grandma did not care about and could not do housework or cooking at all. In fact, she seemed to have inherited all the characteristics of a 'Southern lady'—even to the petite hands and feet. She was a staunch Presbyterian—the entire family being permitted to attend the white church, which fact attests to their high standing among the whites in the community, and consequently they were 'looked up to' by the Negroes. Grandma maintained her independence until the time of her death, near the age of eighty-three." I especially remember her as being very thrifty. I judge that she handled the finances mostly in her family, because my mother has often evoked many a good laugh from me by relating instances where her father would have to ask her for money and she would dole it out in little bits.

The Negro grandmother has not ceased to watch over the destiny of the Negro families as they have moved in ever increasing numbers to the cities during the present century. For example, she was present in sixty-one of the families of 342 junior high school students in Nashville. In twenty-five of these a grandfather was also present. But in twenty-four of the remaining thirty-six families, we find her in eight families with only the mother of the children; in seven with only the father; and in nine she was the only adult member. However, figures cannot give us any conception of the grandmother, unawed and still with her ancient dignity, watching over her children in the strange world of the city. We shall, therefore, let one who has met her daily and portrayed her in all her dignity give a final testimonial:

Great-grandmother hobbles in on crutches, her garments pinned across her chest with a safety pin, and her cap tied on with a black ribbon. But it takes more than crutches and discarded ribbons to abash a colored grandmother. In fact, they are the only grandmothers whom I have ever known to come into their own. They are still persons. They never quail before a stylish granddaughter by so much as a fraction of an inch. If they look like scarecrows, it embarrasses neither the one nor the other. Let the girl be saucy, and one look from her grandmother's dark heavy-lidded eyes hits its mark. Accustomed as I am to the spectacle of white grandmothers idealized according to Whistler, but relegated in spite of themselves to shawls and chimney corners, these doughty old colored women, physically infirm but spiritually undaunted, who have somehow managed to keep a hold on their progeny, are impressive creatures. I even find it refreshingly rakish, that so many of our fights start over the debated reputation of an old creature muffled in a ragbag. Her girlish escapades still have the power to set her offspring fighting, and one feels that neither she nor they think less of each other for the scrimmage. No other race comes to court whose battles are waged so often in vindication of such ancient dames. And personally I never fail to derive a piquant savor from jousts of chivalry over the long dead flirtations of such bags of bones. Of all people these old women represent the eternal feminine. They have drunk of the fount of youth and have never lost its flavor. Nothing, one feels, but their rheumatism keeps them from joining in the dance of life with their great-grandchildren. Often a white woman loses her head in court and acts uncommonly silly. A colored woman never. She accepts what must be accepted, tosses or nods her head according to how the outcome suits her (they are not hard to please), and marches or hobbles out of the room as she came in, with her dignity unimpaired.[7]

Thus the Negro grandmother stands today, as of old, as the "oldest head" in the House of the Mother. . . .

7. Eleanor Rowland Wembridge, *Life among the Lowbrows* (Boston and New York, 1931) pp. 169-70.

12

"By glistening, dancing seas . . ."

by Lethonia Gee
(First published 1968)

FROM

Black Fire
edited by LeRoi Jones and Larry Neal

Despite the environmentally forced confusion of male-female roles and the obvious conflict between the sexes in the black community, the chief concern of most black women has been the black man—whether for his safety or his affection. In understanding the black woman, this feeling for the black man is perhaps paramount; it is certainly an aspect of black life that is central to a healthy reparation of black male-female relationships. The following poem expresses with clarity and simplicity the depth of that concern.

> By glistening, dancing seas
> On ancient time-spun sands
> Black woman bends her wooly head
> And thinks about her man
>
> In the ghost house of the ghetto
> With folded, wrinkled hands
> Black woman bends her tired head
> And thinks about her man

On ugly, cement, city streets
Or quiet village-lands
Black woman has one heavy thought
And it's about her man

I V

A HERITAGE
REDISCOVERED:

THE NEW BLACK WOMAN

ALTHOUGH the black woman has suffered more than most from the irrational character of racism, many black women have sustained a prevailing pride in themselves as women and human beings. For some that stance has led to conflicts and, ultimately, death; others have managed to live with dignity despite the overwhelming forces that confronted them.

In recent years the task has become somewhat easier; Afro-Americans have become more resolute and outspoken in their push for equal rights. The firmness of their commitment has, of course, affected their posture within society. Black women have often been at the forefront in the drive for equality, and they no less than black males have benefited from the self-determination and positive redefinition that has grown out of the movement.

The black woman, in fact, may well be in position to benefit more from the recent upheavals in American society than the black male. Just as she has been the victim of prejudice based on both her sex and her race, she may now reap the advantages of the trend toward women's liberation and the Afro-

218 TO BE A BLACK WOMAN: PORTRAITS IN FACT AND FICTION

American's advance toward equality and self-determination. The following selections are focused on the heritage after which the new black woman might mold herself; they also clarify the role that the black male must assume if such a redefinition is to be possible.

1

"The Damnation of Women"

by W. E. B. Du Bois
(First published 1920)

FROM

Darkwater

Throughout her years of oppression, even when forced into the most degrading circumstances, the black woman has maintained an uncommon sense of inner strength and worth. And perhaps as Du Bois points out: "No other women on earth could have emerged from the hell of force and temptation which once engulfed and still surrounds black women in America with half the modesty and womanliness that they retain."

The following selection is a testament to the proud heritage of perseverance and dignity that represents the other, too often overlooked, face of the black woman. Here, in a selection from a prophetic book published a half century ago, Du Bois eloquently describes the historical source of that heritage and suggests the course of its more complete actualization which today may be seen in every black community.

. . . BUT what of black women? The world that wills to worship womankind studiously forgets its darker sisters. They seem in a sense to typify that veiled Melancholy:

> "Whose saintly visage is too bright
> To hit the sense of human sight,

> And, therefore, to our weaker view
> O'er-laid with black."

Yet the world must heed these daughters of sorrow, from the primal black All-Mother of men down through the ghostly throng of mighty womanhood, who walked in the mysterious dawn of Asia and Africa; from Neith, the primal mother of all, whose feet rest on hell, and whose almighty hands uphold the heavens; all religion, from beauty to beast, lies on her eager breasts; her body bears the stars, while her shoulders are necklaced by the dragon; from black Neith down to

> "That starr'd Ethiop queen who strove
> To set her beauty's praise above
> The sea-nymphs,"

through dusky Cleopatras, dark Candaces, and darker, fiercer Zinghas, to our own day and our own land,—in gentle Phillis; Harriet, the crude Moses; the sybil, Sojourner Truth; and the martyr, Louise De Mortie.

The father and his worship is Asia; Europe is the precocious, self-centered, forward-striving child; but the land of the mother is and was Africa. In subtle and mysterious way, despite her curious history, her slavery, polygamy, and toil, the spell of the African mother pervades her land. Isis, the mother, is still titular goddess, in thought if not in name, of the dark continent. Nor does this all seem to be solely a survival of the historic matriarchate through which all nations pass,—it appears to be more than this,—as if the great black race in passing up the steps of human culture gave the world, not only the Iron Age, the cultivation of the soil, and the domestication of animals, but also, in peculiar emphasis, the mother-idea.

"No mother can love more tenderly and none is more tenderly loved than the Negro mother," writes Schneider. Robin tells of the slave who bought his mother's freedom instead of his own. Mungo Park writes: "Everywhere in Africa, I have noticed that no greater affront can be offered a Negro than insulting his mother. 'Strike me,' cries a Mandingo to his enemy, 'but revile not my mother!' " And the Krus and Fantis say the same. The peoples on the Zambezi and the great lakes cry in sudden fear or joy: "O, my mother!" And the Herero swears (endless oath) "By my mother's tears!" "As the mist in the swamps," cries the Angola Negro, "so lives the love of father and mother."

A student of the present Gold Coast life describes the work of the village headman, and adds: "It is a difficult task that he is set to, but in this matter he has all-powerful helpers in the female members of the family, who will be either the aunts or the sisters or the cousins or the nieces of the headman, and as their interests are identical with his in every particular, the good women spontaneously train up their children to implicit obedience to the headman, whose rule in the family thus becomes a simple and an easy matter. 'The hand that rocks the cradle rules the world.' What a power for good in the native state system would the mothers of the Gold Coast and Ashanti become by judicious training upon native lines!"

Schweinfurth declares of one tribe: "A bond between mother and child which lasts for life is the measure of affection shown among the Dyoor," and Ratzel adds:

"Agreeable to the natural relation the mother stands first among the chief influences affecting the children. From the Zulus to the Waganda, we find the mother the most influential counsellor at the court of ferocious sovereigns, like Chaka or Mtesa; sometimes sisters take her place. Thus even with chiefs who possess wives by hundreds the bonds of blood are the strongest and that the woman, though often heavily burdened, is in herself held in no small esteem among the Negroes is clear from the numerous Negro queens, from the medicine women, from the participation in public meetings permitted to women by many Negro peoples."

As I remember through memories of others, backward

among my own family, it is the mother I ever recall,—the little, far-off mother of my grandmothers, who sobbed her life
away in song, longing for her lost palm-trees and scented waters; the tall and bronzen grandmother, with beaked nose and
shrewish eyes, who loved and scolded her black and laughing
husband as he smoked lazily in his high oak chair; above all,
my own mother, with all her soft brownness,—the brown velvet of her skin, the sorrowful black-brown of her eyes, and
the tiny brown-capped waves of her midnight hair as it lay
new parted on her forehead. All the way back in these dim
distances it is mothers and mothers of mothers who seem to
count, while fathers are shadowy memories.

Upon this African mother-idea, the westward slave trade
and American slavery struck like doom. In the cruel exigen-
cies of the traffic in men and in the sudden, unprepared
emancipation the great pendulum of social equilibrium
swung from a time, in 1800,—when America had but eight or
less black women to every ten black men,—all too swiftly to a
day, in 1870,—when there were nearly eleven women to ten
men in our Negro population. This was but the outward
numerical fact of social dislocation; within lay polygamy,
polyandry, concubinage, and moral degradation. They fought
against all this desperately, did these black slaves in the West
Indies, especially among the half-free artisans; they set up
their ancient household gods, and when Toussaint and Chris-
tophe founded their kingdom in Haiti, it was based on old
African tribal ties and beneath it was the mother-idea.

The crushing weight of slavery fell on black women. Under it there was no legal marriage, no legal family, no legal
control over children. To be sure, custom and religion replaced here and there what the law denied, yet one has but to
read advertisements like the following to see the hell beneath
the system:

"One hundred dollars reward will be given for my two
fellows, Abram and Frank. Abram has a wife at Colonel Stew-

art's, in Liberty County, and a mother at Thunderbolt, and a sister in Savannah.

"WILLIAM ROBERTS."

"Fifty dollars reward—Ran away from the subscriber, a Negro girl named Maria. She is of a copper color, between thirteen and fourteen years of age—bareheaded and barefooted. She is small for her age—very sprightly and very likely. She stated she was going to see her mother at Maysville.

"SANFORD THOMSON."

"Fifty dollars reward—Ran away from the subscriber his Negro man Pauladore, commonly called Paul. I understand General R. Y. Hayne has purchased his wife and children from H. L. Pinckney, Esq., and has them now on his plantation at Goose Creek, where, no doubt, the fellow is frequently lurking.

"T. DAVIS."

The Presbyterian synod of Kentucky said to the churches under its care in 1835: "Brothers and sisters, parents and children, husbands and wives, are torn asunder and permitted to see each other no more. These acts are daily occurring in the midst of us. The shrieks and agony often witnessed on such occasions proclaim, with a trumpet tongue, the iniquity of our system. There is not a neighborhood where these heartrending scenes are not displayed. There is not a village or road that does not behold the sad procession of manacled outcasts whose mournful countenances tell that they are exiled by force from all that their hearts hold dear."

A sister of a president of the United States declared: "We Southern ladies are complimented with the names of wives, but we are only the mistresses of seraglios."

Out of this, what sort of black women could be born into the world of today? There are those who hasten to answer this query in scathing terms and who say lightly and repeatedly that out of black slavery came nothing decent in womanhood;

that adultery and uncleanness were their heritage and are their continued portion.

Fortunately so exaggerated a charge is humanly impossible of truth. The half-million women of Negro descent who lived at the beginning of the 19th century had become the mothers of two and one-fourth million daughters at the time of the Civil War and five million granddaughters in 1910. Can all these women be vile and the hunted race continue to grow in wealth and character? Impossible. Yet to save from the past the shreds and vestiges of self-respect has been a terrible task. I most sincerely doubt if any other race of women could have brought its fineness up through so devilish a fire.

Alexander Crummell once said of his sister in the blood: "In her girlhood all the delicate tenderness of her sex has been rudely outraged. In the field, in the rude cabin, in the press-room, in the factory she was thrown into the companionship of coarse and ignorant men. No chance was given her for delicate reserve or tender modesty. From her childhood she was the doomed victim of the grossest passion. All the virtues of her sex were utterly ignored. If the instinct of chastity asserted itself, then she had to fight like a tiger for the ownership and possession of her own person and ofttimes had to suffer pain and lacerations for her virtuous self-assertion. When she reached maturity, all the tender instincts of her womanhood were ruthlessly violated. At the age of marriage,—always prematurely anticipated under slavery—she was mated as the stock of the plantation were mated, not to be the companion of a loved and chosen husband, but to be the breeder of human cattle for the field or the auction block."

Down in such mire has the black motherhood of this race struggled,—starving its own wailing offspring to nurse to the world their swaggering masters; welding for its children chains which affronted even the moral sense of an unmoral world. Many a man and woman in the South have lived in wedlock as holy as Adam and Eve and brought forth their brown and golden children, but because the darker woman was helpless, her chivalrous and whiter mate could cast her off at his pleasure and publicly sneer at the body he had privately blasphemed.

I shall forgive the white South much in its final judgment day: I shall forgive its slavery, for slavery is a world-old habit; I shall forgive its fighting for a well-lost cause, and for remembering that struggle with tender tears; I shall forgive its so-called "pride of race," the passion of its hot blood, and even its dear, old, laughable strutting and posing; but one thing I shall never forgive, neither in this world nor the world to come: its wanton and continued and persistent insulting of the black womanhood which it sought and seeks to prostitute to its lust. I cannot forget that it is such Southern gentlemen into whose hands smug Northern hypocrites of today are seeking to place our women's eternal destiny,—men who insist upon withholding from my mother and wife and daughter those signs and appellations of courtesy and respect which elsewhere he withholds only from bawds and courtesans.

The result of this history of insult and degradation has been both fearful and glorious. It has birthed the haunting prostitute, the brawler, and the beast of burden; but it has also given the world an efficient womanhood, whose strength lies in its freedom and whose chastity was won in the teeth of temptation and not in prison and swaddling clothes.

To no modern race does its women mean so much as to the Negro nor come so near to the fulfilment of its meaning. As one of our women writes: "Only the black woman can say 'when and where I enter, in the quiet, undisputed dignity of my womanhood, without violence and without suing or special patronage, then and there the whole Negro race enters with me.'"

They came first, in earlier days, like foam flashing on dark, silent waters,—bits of stern, dark womanhood here and there tossed almost carelessly aloft to the world's notice. First and naturally they assumed the panoply of the ancient African

mother of men, strong and black, whose very nature beat back
the wilderness of oppression and contempt. Such a one was
that cousin of my grandmother, whom western Massachusetts
remembers as "Mum Bett." Scarred for life by a blow received
in defense of a sister, she ran away to Great Barrington and
was the first slave, or one of the first, to be declared free
under the Bill of Rights of 1780. The son of the judge who
freed her, writes:

"Even in her humble station, she had, when occasion required
it, an air of command which conferred a degree of dignity and
gave her an ascendancy over those of her rank, which is very unusual in persons of any rank or color. Her determined and resolute character, which enabled her to limit the ravages of Shay's
mob, was manifested in her conduct and deportment during her
whole life. She claimed no distinction, but it was yielded to her
from her superior experience, energy, skill, and sagacity. Having
known this woman as familiarly as I knew either of my parents,
I cannot believe in the moral or physical inferiority of the race to
which she belonged. The degradation of the African must have
been otherwise caused than by natural inferiority."

It was such strong women that laid the foundations of the
great Negro church of today, with its five million members
and ninety millions of dollars in property. One of the early
mothers of the church, Mary Still, writes thus quaintly, in the
[eighteen-] forties:

"When we were as castouts and spurned from the large
churches, driven from our knees, pointed at by the proud, neg-
lected by the careless, without a place of worship, Allen, faithful
to the heavenly calling, came forward and laid the foundation of
this connection. The women, like the women at the sepulcher,
were early to aid in laying the foundation of the temple and in
helping to carry up the noble structure and in the name of their
God set up their banner; most of our aged mothers are gone from
this to a better state of things. Yet some linger still on their staves,
watching with intense interest the ark as it moves over the tem-
pestuous waves of opposition and ignorance. . . .

"But the labors of these women stopped not here, for they knew well that they were subject to affliction and death. For the purpose of mutual aid, they banded themselves together in society capacity, that they might be better able to administer to each others' sufferings and to soften their own pillows. So we find the females in the early history of the church abounding in good works and in acts of true benevolence."

From such spiritual ancestry came two striking figures of war-time,—Harriet Tubman and Sojourner Truth.

For eight or ten years previous to the breaking out of the Civil War, Harriet Tubman was a constant attendant at anti-slavery conventions, lectures, and other meetings; she was a black woman of medium size, smiling countenance, with her upper front teeth gone, attired in coarse but neat clothes, and carrying always an old-fashioned reticule at her side. Usually as soon as she sat down she would drop off in sound sleep.

She was born a slave in Maryland, in 1820, bore the marks of the lash on her flesh; and had been made partially deaf, and perhaps to some degree mentally unbalanced, by a blow on the head in childhood. Yet she was one of the most important agents of the Underground Railroad and a leader of fugitive slaves. She ran away in 1849 and went to Boston in 1854, where she was welcomed into the homes of the leading abolitionists and where every one listened with tense interest to her strange stories. She was absolutely illiterate, with no knowledge of geography, and yet year after year she penetrated the slave states and personally led North over three hundred fugitives without losing a single one. A standing reward of $10,000 was offered for her, but as she said: "The whites cannot catch us, for I was born with the charm, and the Lord has given me the power." She was one of John Brown's closest advisers and only severe sickness prevented her presence at Harper's Ferry.

When the war cloud broke, she hastened to the front, flitting down along her own mysterious paths, haunting the armies in the field, and serving as guide and nurse and spy.

She followed Sherman in his great march to the sea and was with Grant at Petersburg, and always in the camps the Union officers silently saluted her.

The other woman belonged to a different type,—a tall, gaunt, black, unsmiling sybil, weighted with the woe of the world. She ran away from slavery and giving up her own name took the name of Sojourner Truth. She says: "I can remember when I was a little, young girl, how my old mammy would sit out of doors in the evenings and look up at the stars and groan, and I would say, 'Mammy, what makes you groan so?' And she would say, 'I am groaning to think of my poor children; they do not know where I be and I don't know where they be. I look up at the stars and they look up at the stars!' "

Her determination was founded on unwavering faith in ultimate good. Wendell Phillips says that he was once in Faneuil Hall, when Frederick Douglass was one of the chief speakers. Douglass had been describing the wrongs of the Negro race and as he proceeded he grew more and more excited and finally ended by saying that they had no hope of justice from the whites, no possible hope except in their own right arms. It must come to blood! They must fight for themselves. Sojourner Truth was sitting, tall and dark, on the very front seat facing the platform, and in the hush of feeling when Douglass sat down she spoke out in her deep, peculiar voice, heard all over the hall:

"Frederick, is God dead?"

Such strong, primitive types of Negro womanhood in America seem to some to exhaust its capabilities. They know less of a not more worthy, but a finer type of black woman wherein trembles all of that delicate sense of beauty and striving for self-realization, which is as characteristic of the Negro soul as is its quaint strength and sweet laughter. George Washington wrote in grave and gentle courtesy to a Negro woman, in 1776, that he would "be happy to see" at his headquarters at any time, a person "to whom nature has been so liberal and beneficial in her dispensations." This child, Phillis Wheatley, sang her trite and halting strain to a world that wondered and could not produce her like. Measured today her muse was slight and yet, feeling her striving spirit, we call to her still in her own words:

"Through thickest glooms look back, immortal shade."

Perhaps even higher than strength and art loom human sympathy and sacrifice as characteristic of Negro womanhood. Long years ago, before the Declaration of Independence, Kate Ferguson was born in New York. Freed, widowed, and bereaved of her children before she was twenty, she took the children of the streets of New York, white and black, to her empty arms, taught them, found them homes, and with Dr. Mason of Murray Street Church established the first modern Sunday School in Manhattan.

Sixty years later came Mary Shadd up out of Delaware. She was tall and slim, of that ravishing dream-born beauty,— that twilight of the races which we call mulatto. Well-educated, vivacious, with determination shining from her sharp eyes, she threw herself singlehanded into the great Canadian pilgrimage when thousands of hunted black men hurried northward and crept beneath the protection of the lion's paw. She became teacher, editor, and lecturer; tramping afoot through winter snows, pushing without blot or blemish through crowd and turmoil to conventions and meetings, and finally becoming recruiting agent for the United States government in gathering Negro soldiers in the West.

After the war the sacrifice of Negro women for freedom and uplift is one of the finest chapters in their history. Let one life typify all: Louise De Mortie, a free-born Virginia girl, had lived most of her life in Boston. Her high forehead, swelling lips, and dark eyes marked her for a woman of feeling and intellect. She began a successful career as a public reader. Then came the War and the Call. She went to the orphaned colored children of New Orleans,—out of freedom into insult and oppression and into the teeth of the yellow fever. She toiled and dreamed. In 1887 she had raised money and built an orphan home and that same year, in the thirty-fourth of her young life, she died, saying simply: "I belong to God."

As I look about me today in this veiled world of mine, despite the noisier and more spectacular advance of my brothers, I instinctively feel and know that it is the five million women of my race who really count. Black women (and women whose grandmothers were black) are today furnishing our teachers; they are the main pillars of those social settlements which we call churches; and they have with small doubt raised three-fourths of our church property. If we have today, as seems likely, over a billion dollars of accumulated goods, who shall say how much of it has been wrung from the hearts of servant girls and washerwomen and women toilers in the fields? As makers of two million homes these women are today seeking in marvelous ways to show forth our strength and beauty and our conception of the truth.

In the United States in 1910 there were 4,931,882 women of Negro descent; over twelve hundred thousand of these were children, another million were girls and young women under twenty, and two and a half million were adults. As a mass these women were unlettered,—a fourth of those from fifteen to twenty-five years of age were unable to write. These women are passing through, not only a moral, but an economic revolution. Their grandmothers married at twelve and fifteen, but twenty-seven per cent of these women today who have passed fifteen are still single.

Yet these black women toil and toil hard. There were in 1910 two and a half million Negro homes in the United States. Out of these homes walked daily to work two million women and girls over ten years of age,—over half of the colored female population as against a fifth in the case of white women. These, then, are a group of workers, fighting for their daily bread like men; independent and approaching economic freedom! They furnished a million farm laborers, 80,000 farmers, 22,000 teachers, 600,000 servants and washerwomen, and 50,000 in trades and merchandizing.

The family group, however, which is the ideal of the culture with which these folk have been born, is not based on the idea of an economically independent working mother. Rather its ideal harks back to the sheltered harem with the mother emerging at first as nurse and homemaker, while the man remains the sole breadwinner. What is the inevitable result of the clash of such ideals and such facts in the colored group? Broken families.

Among native white women one in ten is separated from her husband by death, divorce, or desertion. Among Negroes the ratio is one in seven. Is the cause racial? No, it is economic, because there is the same high ratio among the white foreign-born. The breaking up of the present family is the result of modern working and sex conditions and it hits the laborers with terrible force. The Negroes are put in a peculiarly difficult position, because the wage of the male breadwinner is below the standard, while the openings for colored women in certain lines of domestic work, and now in industries, are many. Thus while toil holds the father and brother in country and town at low wages, the sisters and mothers are called to the city. As a result the Negro women outnumber the men nine or ten to eight in many cities, making what Charlotte Gilman bluntly calls "cheap women."

What shall we say to this new economic equality in a great laboring class? Some people within and without the race deplore it. "Back to the homes with the women," they cry, "and higher wage for the men." But how impossible this is has been shown by war conditions. Cessation of foreign migration has raised Negro men's wages, to be sure—but it has not only raised Negro women's wages, it has opened to them a score of new avenues of earning a living. Indeed, here in microcosm and with differences emphasizing sex equality, is the industrial history of labor in the 19th and 20th centuries. We cannot abolish the new economic freedom of women. We cannot imprison women again in a home or require them all on pain of death to be nurses and housekeepers.

What is today the message of these black women to America and to the world? The uplift of women is, next to the problem of the color line and the peace movement, our greatest modern cause. When, now, two of these movements—woman and color—combine in one, the combination has deep meaning.

In other years women's way was clear: to be beautiful, to be petted, to bear children. Such has been their theoretic destiny and if perchance they have been ugly, hurt, and barren, that has been forgotten with studied silence. In partial compensation for this narrowed destiny the white world has lavished its politeness on its womankind,—its chivalry and bows, its uncoverings and courtesies—all the accumulated homage disused for courts and kings and craving exercise. The revolt of white women against this preordained destiny has in these latter days reached splendid proportions, but it is the revolt of an aristocracy of brains and ability,—the middle class and rank and file still plod on in the appointed path, paid by the homage, the almost mocking homage, of men.

From black women of America, however, (and from some others, too, but chiefly from black women and their daughters' daughters) this gauze has been withheld and without semblance of such apology they have been frankly trodden under the feet of men. They are and have been objected to, apparently for reasons peculiarly exasperating to reasoning human beings. When in this world a man comes forward with a thought, a deed, a vision, we ask not, how does he look, —but what is his message? It is of but passing interest whether or not the messenger is beautiful or ugly,—the *message* is the thing. This, which is axiomatic among men, has been in past ages but partially true if the messenger was a woman. The world still wants to ask that a woman primarily be pretty and if she is not, the mob pouts and asks querulously, "What else

are women for?" Beauty "is its own excuse for being," but
there are other excuses, as most men know, and when the
white world objects to black women because it does not consider them beautiful, the black world of right asks two questions: "What is beauty?" and, "Suppose you think them ugly,
what then? If ugliness and unconventionality and eccentric-
ity of face and deed do not hinder men from doing the world's
work and reaping the world's reward, why should it hinder
women?"

Other things being equal, all of us, black and white, would
prefer to be beautiful in face and form and suitably clothed;
but most of us are not so, and one of the mightiest revolts of
the century is against the devilish decree that no woman is a
woman who is not by present standards a beautiful woman.
This decree the black women of America have in large measure escaped from the first. Not being expected to be merely
ornamental, they have girded themselves for work, instead of
adorning their bodies only for play. Their sturdier minds
have concluded that if a woman be clean, healthy, and educated, she is as pleasing as God wills and far more useful than
most of her sisters. If in addition to this she is pink and white
and straight-haired, and some of her fellow-men prefer this,
well and good; but if she is black or brown and crowned in
curled mists (and this to us is the most beautiful thing on
earth), this is surely the flimsiest excuse for spiritual incar-
ceration or banishment.

The very attempt to do this in the case of Negro Americans
has strangely over-reached itself. By so much as the defective
eyesight of the white world rejects black women as beauties,
by so much the more it needs them as human beings,—an en-
viable alternative, as many a white woman knows. Consequently, for black women alone, as a group, "handsome is
that handsome does" and they are asked to be no more beautiful than God made them, but they are asked to be efficient,
to be strong, fertile, muscled, and able to work. If they marry,
they must as independent workers be able to help support

their children, for their men are paid on a scale which makes sole support of the family often impossible.

On the whole, colored working women are paid as well as white working women for similar work, save in some higher grades, while colored men get from one-fourth to three-fourths less than white men. The result is curious and three-fold: the economic independence of black women is increased, the breaking up of Negro families must be more frequent, and the number of illegitimate children is decreased more slowly among them than other evidences of culture are increased, just as was once true in Scotland and Bavaria.

What does this mean? It forecasts a mighty dilemma which the whole world of civilization, despite its will, must one time frankly face: the unhusbanded mother or the childless wife. God send us a world with woman's freedom and married motherhood inextricably wed, but until He sends it, I see more of future promise in the betrayed girl-mothers of the black belt than in the childless wives of the white North, and I have more respect for the colored servant who yields to her frank longing for motherhood than for her white sister who offers up children for clothes. Out of a sex freedom that today makes us shudder will come in time a day when we will no longer pay men for work they do not do, for the sake of their harem; we will pay women what they earn and insist on their working and earning it; we will allow those persons to vote who know enough to vote, whether they be black or female, white or male; and we will ward off race suicide, not by further burdening the over-burdened, but by honoring motherhood, even when the sneaking father shirks his duty.

"Wait till the lady passes," said a Nashville white boy.

"She's no lady; she's a nigger," answered another.

So some few women are born free, and some amid insult and scarlet letters achieve freedom; but our women in black had freedom thrust contemptuously upon them. With that freedom they are buying an untrammeled independence and dear as is the price they pay for it, it will in the end be worth every taunt and groan. Today the dreams of the mothers are coming true. We have still our poverty and degradation, our lewdness and our cruel toil; but we have, too, a vast group of women of Negro blood who for strength of character, cleanness of soul, and unselfish devotion of purpose, is today easily the peer of any group of women in the civilized world. And more than that, in the great rank and file of our five million women we have the up-working of new revolutionary ideals, which must in time have vast influence on the thought and action of this land.

For this, their promise, and for their hard past, I honor the women of my race. Their beauty,—their dark and mysterious beauty of midnight eyes, crumpled hair, and soft, full-featured faces—is perhaps more to me than to you, because I was born to its warm and subtle spell; but their worth is yours as well as mine. No other women on earth could have emerged from the hell of force and temptation which once engulfed and still surrounds black women in America with half the modesty and womanliness that they retain. I have always felt like bowing myself before them in all abasement, searching to bring some tribute to these long-suffering victims, these burdened sisters of mine, whom the world, the wise, white world, loves to affront and ridicule and wantonly to insult. I have known the women of many lands and nations,—I have known and seen and lived beside them, but none have I known more sweetly feminine, more unswervingly loyal, more desperately earnest, and more instinctively pure in body and in soul than the daughters of my black mothers. This, then,—a little thing—to their memory and inspiration.

2

"Eliza Harris"

by Frances E. W. Harper
(First published 1854)

FROM

Poems on Various Subjects

*Since any resistance or defiance, particularly during slavery,
meant risking one's life, the courage displayed by Sojourner
Truth, Harriet Tubman, and many less known black women
was truly exaraordinary. The following poem depicts many
of the hazards that confronted those who chose to seek their
freedom rather than submit to the degradation of slavery. It
is, moreover, a tribute to the dignity and strength of character that has impelled many black women to challenge
openly America's racial exploitation.*

ELIZA HARRIS

Like a fawn from the arrow, startled and wild,
A woman swept by us, bearing a child;
In her eye was the night of a settled despair,
And her brow was o'ershaded with anguish and care.

She was nearing the river—in reaching the brink,
She heeded no danger, she paused not to think;

For she is a mother—her child is a slave—
And she'll give him his freedom, or find him a grave!

It was a vision to haunt us, that innocent face—
So pale in its aspect, so fair in its grace;
As the tramp of the horse and the bay of the hound,
With the fetters that gall, were trailing the ground!

She was nerv'd by despair, and strengthened by woe,
As she leap'd o'er the chasms that yawn'd from below;
Death howl'd in the tempest, and rav'd in the blast,
But she heard not the sound till the danger was past.

Oh! how shall I speak of my proud country's shame?
Of the stains on her glory, how give them their name?
How say that her banner in mockery waves—
Her "star spangled banner"—o'er millions of slaves?

How say that the lawless may torture and chase
A woman whose crime is the hue of her face?
How the depths of the forest may echo around,
With the shrieks of despair, and the bay of the hound?

With her step on the ice, and her arm on her child,
The danger was fearful, the pathway was wild;
But, aided by Heaven, she gained a free shore,
Where the friends of humanity open'd their door.

So fragile and lovely, so fearfully pale,
Like a lily that bends to the breath of the gale,
Save the heave of her breast, and the sway of her hair,
You'd have thought her a statue of fear and despair.

In agony close to her bosom she press'd
The life of her heart, the child of her breast:—
Oh! love from its tenderness gathering might,
Had strengthen'd her soul for the dangers of flight.

But she's free!—yes, free from the land where the slave
From the hand of oppression must rest in the grave;

Where bondage and torture, where scourges and chains
Have plac'd on our banner indelible stains.

The bloodhounds have miss'd the scent of her way;
The hunter is rifled and foil'd of his prey;
Fierce jargon and cursing, with clanking of chains,
Make sounds of strange discord on Liberty's plains.

With the rapture of love and fulness of bliss,
She placed on his brow a mother's fond kiss:—
O poverty, danger and death she can brave,
For the child of her love is no longer a slave!

3

"For de Lawd"

by Lucille Clifton
(First published 1969)

FROM
Good Times

Black women of mid-twentieth-century America are now acknowledging the heritage bequeathed to them by their African ancestors. Where once it was a latent force providing the stoic strength necessary to endure continued debasement, it is becoming an externalized and esteemed virtue, as Lucille Clifton suggests in her poignant poem.

"FOR DE LAWD"

people say they have a hard time
understanding how I
go on about my business
playing my Ray Charles
hollering at the kids—
seem like my Afro
cut off in some old image
would show I got a long memory
and I come from a line
of black and going on women
who got used to making it through murdered sons

and who grief kept on pushing
who fried chicken
ironed
swept off the back steps
who grief kept
for their still alive sons
for their sons coming
for their sons gone
just pushing

4

FROM

Silent Voices: The Southern Negro Woman Today

by Josephine Carson

(First published 1969)

The new black woman is many things: She may have availed herself of increased opportunity for higher education, she may hold a professional position or she may simply be a housewife, but she is almost certain to be aware of the radical changes in the assessment of women in general and black women in particular. The following selection, an interview with an Atlanta woman, illustrates the multiple concerns of the modern black woman's liberated point of view. Sarah not only reflects the modern woman's concern with the contradictions of career and marriage, but also clearly articulates the black woman's particular concern with the narrowness of the Western standard of beauty and prospect of black absorption in American society.

SARAH is twenty-five, has a master's degree in English from Spellman College. She describes herself as a "careful radical." She was married two years ago and has a baby son who is named after a well-known African leader.

"I know what it suggests when I say that my mother is keeping him while my husband and I work—that we're living in the same old matriarchal style. But nowadays all these grandmothers can say that they're bringing up their grandchildren so the parents can work in the Movement and it sounds better . . ." She laughs ruefully. "And . . . it *is* better.

"In this organization I'm a sort of coordinator of finances. I decide what we can spend for what and usually I have to tell them that we can't afford it no matter what it is!" She slowly relaxes and levels with me, but her pride is exercised perpetually, a kindly warning to me. Talk of marriage opens her up.

"Well, I've found out there's no answer, really, for a woman who works in a career and has children. Like: my baby knows who his mother is, I think, but it's his grandmother who's giving him the food and that means something very special. He's getting more of her . . . uh . . . nature than he is of mine. He's learning to live with *her,* not me. But I hope I can stay very close to him. I take him on weekends and spend a lot of time with him. And he's crazy about his daddy already.

"Sometimes I worry about it, though. My mother is a very special woman. Very powerful."

"Did she influence you as much as your father?"

"Oh, more, I think. She has so much social conscience, for one thing. I remember when I was little—our house was on the escape route for Negro men on the prison chain gangs. You know, Negroes used to be really brutalized on the chain gangs not so long ago, and they escaped when they could. It's still pretty bad for Negro men in prison. Well, my mother always kept a suit of men's clothes in the house and a package of things—a little silver money, matches, names and telephones, maybe of certain preachers around the South who would help—you know?

"Once or twice I remember a lotta commotion in the house and whisperin' and a strange man in the kitchen in the middle of the night.

"She took a big risk. Didn't matter what he did or who he was—he was a Negro man off the chain gang and if they caught him, they'd beat him to death. So she helped him escape.

"But my daddy was very angry about it. He was afraid we'd

all be killed if they caught us. So, see, she's a strong woman and she *could* influence my son if I'm not with him enough. She's good but he *is* my son." We laugh.

"But marriage is funny. I can't really figure it out. Like, it is so hard to find a strong man that I think sometimes the only reason I married the man I did was 'cause he was the only fellow I met who is stronger than I am. I mean, I love him but we aren't very much alike."

"You think it is essential that a man be stronger than his wife?"

"In a certain way, because women are *so* strong. Negro women, anyway." She laughs guiltily. "I mean, you know, a man has to be *powerful* to handle a woman. We're smarter. There's no question about that. We are. And Negro women can be pretty hard on a man. I mean, white women don't do so much of this as far as I know, but we *fight!* We scream and fight. Lotsa Negro women beat their men!" We laugh knowingly together. "I notice that Jewish women can do that. They scream and carry on. But white gentile women are more . . . uh, cool."

"Maybe they're intimidated."

"Well, to be honest, I think a lotta white women are screwed up terribly, but . . . that's their problem. I don't worry much about them. I spent three years hatin' white women so much it nearly made me crazy. It came from discovering how the whole world had this white idea of beauty. See, the western world concept of beauty is *your* kind of beauty, not mine. You can't find my African kind of beauty— I mean thick lips and kinky hair—in a picture anywhere except a little bit lately with fashion models. But the ads and all that—they still think in terms of narrow noses and light skin and straight hair. Most Negro women straighten their hair and they're going right on with it. Bleaching cream still sells in the stores. And I mean, I just hated that so much that for three years I wouldn't speak to a white woman.

"And then I realized what I was doing to myself. I was losing my self-respect and even losing my looks. I finally had to work myself out of it. I had to find a new sense of my own dignity, and what I really had to do was start *seeing* all over again, in a new way. That's one thing Negroes are trying to do now—to *see* differently. That's hard!"

"Do you think whites are also trying to see differently?"

She deliberates. "Yes . . . yes, I think they are. They don't want to, but some are really trying."

"What do you see as the future of Negro people in America?"

She gives me a wry smile and drops her eyes.

"You wanta know what I really think?"

"Of course."

"I think we will disappear. Because as we are now, we aren't Americans because we aren't white. And, even though I support Black Power and believe in it, I know it is just a temporary necessity for Negro people to get some independence and dignity and catch up to the level of whites. Like, high school education for Negroes is the same as eighth grade for whites, even today. Well, all that is going to change by Black Power pressure, I think. But the more equality we get, the more we are going to fade into the big group. We are too small to stay Negro.

"I mean, look, we are 'something else.' You know that?"

"Well," I am reluctant to agree, "I'll accept your belief, at least."

"Look, everything we need is the very thing that is going to make us less something else, and more what you might call white. And then, just physically, we will intermarry. The trend now is to keep black people together but that won't last either. We will intermarry and very few of us are very black anyway. So, as a psychological type and also a physical type, we are going to get into the big American soul and disappear. There's no other way to go if you stay in America.

"So, in a way I'm working for the extinction of the African type in America because I want black people to have their own businesses and hold high political offices, but I know that when they do, they are going to become more and more a part of the American character. And the black soul is going to die in the middle of the white soul."

She says it softly; it is a dirge.

I consider it. "Don't you think though, that that is in a certain way the fate of all humans? I'll be outlived by the world, by life, it will absorb me and transcend my existence and my individuality. One becomes a part of the nature of the world and very rarely is there a person who remains an individual force and gains immortality by becoming something that happens to the world. Very few individuals or groups have enough impact to remain inviolate from the big digestion of man's evolution and history."

"That's right. But see, I got this double life—as a human being and also as a special group outside the main group."

"Yes, I see."

"And to know that Negroes are going to vanish here is like knowing that your family is going to be wiped out. Because your white identity isn't going to be wiped out here; that is, not for a long time. You are a minority in the world but by the time the majority can wipe you out it will be a little whiter. It will *have* to be a *little* bit white just to get its hands on the wealth that it needs to wipe you out. You see what I'm saying?"

"Yes," I say, "but I guess I see it as the history of humanity and nature, and as a way of saying that mutation is the only means of refining the species. Probably all distinctions of color and type, perhaps even what we know as the biological types of male and female, will be altered and perhaps appear to perish in the process of our evolution. The process inevitably kills off something that one, in his time, finds precious or something by which one defines himself, such as black, white, European, female, or whatever."

"Well," she says, "that's true. But for Negroes in America, because our life was always threatened, we feel very frightened by the idea that Negroes will disappear in America. Because it's very heroic that we are still here at all."

"And yet you believe Negroes *will* disappear and you allow yourself to face that belief?"

"Yes, I do. I have a feeling of . . . well, of death, but it strengthens my feeling of life, somehow. My son has something to do with that, too."

"Would you say that you have acquired the tragic view of life?"

She smiles. "Definitely. But I just never gave it such a dignified name. Ha! That's good. You *gave* me something." She is slightly shocked.

Ah, Sarah. You are, at twenty-five, more whole than most of us at eighty.

"Well, you gave me something too, Sarah. Thank you."

We talk for two hours. I do not want to leave but I know that her work is urgent. We talk about the disappearance of the last American peasantry, which is mainly Negro. We talk of Christianity, which she thinks is an alien religion for Negroes; Christian practice allows for very little ritual action. "Action is necessary to Negroes. In church service, I mean."

We talk about literature, which, she confesses wistfully, she has forsaken. She rarely reads anymore. She likes the French existentialists, especially Camus, and senses that that is already a dated sort of taste. She is one of the most thoughtful women I have talked with. . . .

5

"(Title)"

by Bob Bennett
(First published 1968)

FROM

Black Fire
edited by LeRoi Jones and Larry Neal

*Perhaps the most obvious indication of the black woman's
altered attitude is her more "natural" appearance. Hair
straighteners and skin lighteners have not disappeared, but
more and more black women are rejecting the Western standard of beauty and substituting one that is more commen-
surate with their natural appearance. Bob Bennett's poem
expresses the new sense of joy among those who have accepted
the natural look and thereby more fully accepted themselves.*

"(TITLE)"

The girl with the Afro
  Without words speaks of black & blues & boogaloo
    without a note of music   there is rhythm

The girl with the natural
  Without words speaks of black & soul & feeling
        GLAD TO BE BLACK
    Without the slightest conceit   there is pride

The girl with the natural
  Without words says she loves her black self for itself
    And *mine* for itself
    (Makes me feel good)

The girl with the Afro
    Without words says she loves our mother
        And our mother's children
        (She is my sister: I am her brother)
    without romance   there is love

6

"Reena"

by Paule Marshall
(First published 1966)

FROM

American Negro Short Stories
edited by John Henrik Clarke

Rudimentary social reform, the increased accessibility of higher education, and more equitable employment opportunities have mitigated some of the brutal remnants of black subjugation. These changing conditions have also made Afro-Americans more aware of both their history and their contemporary plight. But with awareness has come greater expectations and a new crisis revolving about the question of black identity.

For the black woman, the identity crisis is particularly crucial. It involves not only the dilemma of achieving a viable and independent sense of self as a black person in a white society; her search for identity also challenges the marginally successful matriarchal identity which black women have traditionally maintained. Thus the modern-day black woman—liberated from the severely limited and savage world of oppression and the black male-female conflict that grows out of that world—is now faced with the problem of establishing a black identity free from the blight of white mimicry and salutary in terms of her relationship with black men.

In the following short story, Paule Marshall portrays the

*quandaries now facing black women in America. Through
the character of Reena, we see the complex interaction with
parents and family, white society, white and black males, and
social reform organizations that is typical of the modern
black woman's predicament.*

LIKE most people with unpleasant childhoods, I am on constant guard against the past—the past being for me the people
and places associated with the years I served out my girlhood
in Brooklyn. The places no longer matter that much since
most of them have vanished. The old grammar school, for instance, P.S. 35 ("Dirty 5's" we called it and with justification)
has been replaced by a low, coldly functional arrangement of
glass and Permastone which bears its name but has none of
the feel of a school about it. The small, grudgingly lighted
stores along Fulton Street, the soda parlor that was like a
church with its stained-glass panels in the door and marble
floor have given way to those impersonal emporiums, the
supermarkets. Our house even, a brownstone relic whose halls
smelled comfortingly of dust and lemon oil, the somnolent
street upon which it stood, the tall, muscular trees which
shaded it were leveled years ago to make way for a city housing project—a stark, graceless warren for the poor. So that
now whenever I revisit that old section of Brooklyn and see
these new and ugly forms, I feel nothing. I might as well be
in a strange city.

But it is another matter with the people of my past, the
faces that in their darkness were myriad reflections of mine.
Whenever I encounter them at the funeral or wake, the
wedding or christening—those ceremonies by which the past
reaffirms its hold—my guard drops and memories banished to
the rear of the mind rush forward to rout the present. I almost become the child again—anxious and angry, disgrace-
fully diffident.

Reena was one of the people from that time, and a main

contributor to my sense of ineffectualness then. She had not done this deliberately. It was just that whenever she talked about herself (and this was not as often as most people) she seemed to be talking about me also. She ruthlessly analyzed herself, sparing herself nothing. Her honesty was so absolute it was a kind of cruelty.

She had not changed, I was to discover in meeting her again after a separation of twenty years. Nor had I really. For although the years had altered our positions (she was no longer the lord and I the lackey) and I could even afford to forgive her now, she still had the ability to disturb me profoundly by dredging to the surface those aspects of myself that I kept buried. This time, as I listened to her talk over the stretch of one long night, she made vivid without knowing it what is perhaps the most critical fact of my existence—that definition of me, of her and millions like us, formulated by others to serve out their fantasies, a definition we have to combat at an unconscionable cost to the self and even use, at times, in order to survive; the cause of so much shame and rage as well as, oddly enough, a source of pride: simply, what it has meant, what it means, to be a black woman in America.

We met—Reena and myself—at the funeral of her aunt who had been my godmother and whom I had also called aunt, Aunt Vi, and loved, for she and her house had been, respectively, a source of understanding and a place of calm for me as a child. Reena entered the church where the funeral service was being held as though she, not the minister, were coming to officiate, sat down among the immediate family up front, and turned to inspect those behind her. I saw her face then.

It was a good copy of the original. The familiar mold was there, that is, and the configuration of bone beneath the skin was the same despite the slight fleshiness I had never seen there before; her features had even retained their distinctive touches: the positive set to her mouth, the assertive lift to her nose, the same insistent, unsettling eyes which when she was

angry became as black as her skin—and this was total, un-
nerving, and very beautiful. Yet something had happened to
her face. It was different despite its sameness. Aging even
while it remained enviably young. Time had sketched in, very
lightly, the evidence of the twenty years.

As soon as the funeral service was over, I left, hurrying out
of the church into the early November night. The wind, already at its winter strength, brought with it the smell of dead
leaves and the image of Aunt Vi there in the church, as dead
as the leaves—as well as the thought of Reena, whom I would
see later at the wake.

Her real name had been Doreen, a standard for girls among
West Indians (her mother, like my parents, was from Bar-
bados), but she had changed it to Reena on her twelfth birthday—"As a present to myself"—and had enforced the change
on her family by refusing to answer to the old name. "Reena.
With two e's!" she would say and imprint those e's on your
mind with the indelible black of her eyes and a thin threatening finger that was like a quill.

She and I had not been friends through our own choice.
Rather, our mothers, who had known each other since childhood, had forced the relationship. And from the beginning,
I had been at a disadvantage. For Reena, as early as the age
of twelve, had had a quality that was unique, superior, and
therefore dangerous. She seemed defined, even then, all of a
piece, the raw edges of her adolescence altogether and made
one dazzling leap from childhood into the very arena of adult
life. At thirteen, for instance, she was reading Zola, Haupt-
mann, Steinbeck, while I was still in the thrall of the Little
Minister and Lorna Doone. When I could only barely con-
ceive of the world beyond Brooklyn, she was talking of the
Civil War in Spain, lynchings in the South, Hitler in Poland
—and talking with the outrage and passion of a revolutionary.
I would try, I remember, to console myself with the thought
that she was really an adult masquerading as a child, which
meant that I could not possibly be her match.

For her part, Reena put up with me and was, by turns, patronizing and impatient. I merely served as the audience before whom she rehearsed her ideas and the yardstick by which she measured her worldliness and knowledge.

"Do you realize that this stupid country supplied Japan with the scrap iron to make the weapons she's now using against it?" she had shouted at me once.

I had not known that.

Just as she overwhelmed me, she overwhelmed her family, with the result that despite a half-dozen brothers and sisters who consumed quantities of bread and jam whenever they visited us, she behaved like an only child and got away with it. Her father, a gentle man with skin the color of dried tobacco and with the nose Reena had inherited jutting out like a crag from his nondescript face, had come from Georgia and was always making jokes about having married a foreigner— Reena's mother being from the West Indies. When not joking, he seemed slightly bewildered by his large family and so in awe of Reena that he avoided her. Reena's mother, a small, dry, formidably black woman, was less a person to me than the abstract principle of force, power, energy. She was alternately strict and indulgent with Reena and, despite the inconsistency, surprisingly effective.

They lived when I knew them in a cold-water railroad flat above a kosher butcher on Belmont Avenue in Brownsville, some distance from us—and this in itself added to Reena's exotic quality. For it was a place where Sunday became Saturday, with all the stores open and pushcarts piled with vegetables and yard goods lined up along the curb, a crowded place where people hawked and spat freely in the streaming gutters and the men looked as if they had just stepped from the pages of the Old Testament with their profuse beards and long, black, satin coats.

When Reena was fifteen her family moved to Jamaica in Queens and since, in those days, Jamaica was considered too far away for visiting, our families lost contact and I did not see Reena again until we were both in college and then only once and not to speak to. . . .

I had walked some distance and by the time I got to the wake which was being held at Aunt Vi's house it was well under way. It was a good wake. Aunt Vi would have been pleased. There was plenty to drink, and more than enough to eat, including some Barbadian favorites: coconut bread, pone made with the cassava root, and the little crisp codfish cakes that are so hot with peppers they bring tears to the eyes as you bite into them.

I had missed the beginning, when everyone had probably sat around talking about Aunt Vi and recalling the few events that had distinguished her otherwise undistinguished life. (Someone, I'm sure, had told of the time she had missed the excursion boat to Atlantic City and had held her own private picnic—complete with pigeon peas and rice and fricassee chicken—on the pier at 42nd Street.) By the time I arrived, though, it would have been indiscreet to mention her name, for by then the wake had become—and this would also have pleased her—a celebration of life.

I had had two drinks, one right after the other, and was well into my third when Reena, who must have been upstairs, entered the basement kitchen where I was. She saw me before I had quite seen her, and with a cry that alerted the entire room to her presence and charged the air with her special force, she rushed toward me.

"Hey, I'm the one who was supposed to be the writer, not you! Do you know, I still can't believe it," she said, stepping back, her blackness heightened by a white mocking smile. "I read both your books over and over again and I can't really believe it. My little Paulie!"

I did not mind. For there was respect and even wonder behind the patronizing words and in her eyes. The old imbalance between us had ended and I was suddenly glad to see her.

I told her so and we both began talking at once, but Reena's voice overpowered mine, so that all I could do after a time was listen while she discussed my books, and dutifully answer her questions about my personal life.

"And what about you?" I said, almost brutally, at the first chance I got. "What've you been up to all this time?"

She got up abruptly. "Good Lord, in here's noisy as hell. Come on, let's go upstairs."

We got fresh drinks and went up to Aunt Vi's bedroom, where in the soft light from the lamps, the huge Victorian bed and the pink satin bedspread with roses of the same material strewn over its surface looked as if they had never been used. And, in a way, this was true. Aunt Vi had seldom slept in her bed or, for that matter, lived in her house, because in order to pay for it, she had had to work at a sleeping-in job which gave her only Thursdays and every other Sunday off.

Reena sat on the bed, crushing the roses, and I sat on one of the numerous trunks which crowded the room. They contained every dress, coat, hat, and shoe that Aunt Vi had worn since coming to the United States. I again asked Reena what she had been doing over the years.

"Do you want a blow by blow account?" she said. But despite the flippancy, she was suddenly serious. And when she began it was clear that she had written out the narrative in her mind many times. The words came too easily; the events, the incidents had been ordered in time, and the meaning of her behavior and of the people with whom she had been involved had been painstakingly analyzed. She talked willingly, with desperation almost. And the words by themselves weren't enough. She used her hands to give them form and urgency. I became totally involved with her and all that she said. So much so that as the night wore on I was not certain at times whether it was she or I speaking.

From the time her family moved to Jamaica until she was nineteen or so, Reena's life sounded, from what she told me in the beginning, as ordinary as mine and most of the girls' we knew. After high school she had gone on to one of the free city colleges, where she had majored in journalism, worked part-time in the school library, and surprisingly enough, joined a houseplan. (Even I hadn't gone that far.) It was an all-Negro club, since there was a tacit understanding that Negro and white girls did not join each other's house-plans. "Integration, Northern style," she said, shrugging.

It seems that Reena had had a purpose and a plan in join-ing the group. "I thought," she said with a wry smile, "I could get those girls up off their complacent rumps and out doing something about social issues. . . . I couldn't get them to budge. I remember after the war when a Negro ex-soldier had his eyes gouged out by a bus driver down South I tried getting them to demonstrate on campus. I talked until I was hoarse, but to no avail. They were too busy planning the an-nual autumn frolic."

Her laugh was bitter but forgiving and it ended in a long reflective silence. After which she said quietly, "It wasn't that they didn't give a damn. It was just, I suppose, that like most people they didn't want to get involved to the extent that they might have to stand up and be counted. If it ever came to that. Then another thing. They thought they were safe, spe-cial. After all, they had grown up in the North, most of them, and so had escaped the Southern-style prejudice; their par-ents, like mine, were struggling to put them through college; they could look forward to being tidy little schoolteachers, social workers, and lab technicians. Oh, they were safe!" The sarcasm scored her voice and then abruptly gave way to pity. "Poor things, they weren't safe, you see, and would never be as long as millions like themselves in Harlem, on Chicago's South Side, down South, all over the place, were unsafe. I tried to tell them this—and they accused me of being over-sensitive. They tried not to listen. But I would have held out and, I'm sure, even brought some of them around eventually if this other business with a silly boy hadn't happened at the same time. . . ."

Reena told me then about her first, brief, and apparently innocent affair with a boy she had met at one of the house-plan parties. It had ended, she said, when the boys' parents had met her. "That was it," she said and the flat of her hand cut into the air. "He was forbidden to see me. The reason? He couldn't bring himself to tell me, but I knew. I was too black.

"Naturally, it wasn't the first time something like that had happened. In fact, you might say that was the theme of my childhood. Because I was dark I was always being plastered with Vaseline so I wouldn't look ashy. Whenever I had my picture taken they would pile a whitish powder on my face and make the lights so bright I always came out looking ghostly. My mother stopped speaking to any number of people because they said I would have been pretty if I hadn't been so dark. Like nearly every little black girl, I had my share of dreams of waking up to find myself with long blonde curls, blue eyes, and skin like milk. So I should have been prepared. Besides, that boy's parents were really rejecting themselves in rejecting me.

"Take us"—and her hands, opening in front of my face as she suddenly leaned forward, seemed to offer me the whole of black humanity. "We live surrounded by white images, and white in this world is synonymous with the good, light, beauty, success, so that, despite ourselves sometimes, we run after that whiteness and deny our darkness, which has been made into the symbol of all that is evil and inferior. I wasn't a person to that boy's parents, but a symbol of the darkness they were in flight from, so that just as they—that boy, his parents, those silly girls in the houseplan—were running from me, I started running from them. . . ."

It must have been shortly after this happened when I saw Reena at a debate which was being held at my college. She did not see me, since she was one of the speakers and I was merely part of her audience in the crowded auditorium. The topic had something to do with intellectual freedom in the colleges (McCarthyism was coming into vogue then) and aside from a Jewish boy from City College, Reena was the most effective—sharp, provocative, her position the most radical. The others on the panel seemed intimidated not only by the strength and cogency of her argument but by the sheer impact of her blackness in their white midst.

Her color might have been a weapon she used to dazzle and disarm her opponents. And she had highlighted it with the clothes she was wearing: a white dress patterned with large blocks of primary colors I remember (it looked Mexican) and a pair of intricately wrought silver earrings—long and with many little parts which clashed like muted cymbals over the microphone each time she moved her head. She wore her hair cropped short like a boy's and it was not straightened like mine and the other Negro girls' in the audience, but left in its coarse natural state: a small forest under which her face emerged in its intense and startling handsomeness. I remember she left the auditorium in triumph that day, surrounded by a noisy entourage from her college—all of them white.

"We were very serious," she said now, describing the left-wing group she had belonged to then—and there was a defensiveness in her voice which sought to protect them from all censure. "We believed—because we were young, I suppose, and had nothing as yet to risk—that we could do something about the injustices which everyone around us seemed to take for granted. So we picketed and demonstrated and bombarded Washington with our protests, only to have our names added to the Attorney General's list for all our trouble. We were always standing on street corners handing out leaflets or getting people to sign petitions. We always seemed to pick the coldest days to do that." Her smile held long after the words had died.

"I, we all, had such a sense of purpose then," she said softly, and a sadness lay aslant the smile now, darkening it. "We were forever holding meetings, having endless discussions, arguing, shouting, theorizing. And we had fun. Those parties! There was always somebody with a guitar. We were always singing. . . ." Suddenly, she began singing—and her voice was sure, militant, and faintly self-mocking.

> *"But the banks are made of marble*
> *With a guard at every door*
> *And the vaults are stuffed with silver*
> *That the workers sweated for. . . ."*

When she spoke again the words were a sad coda to the song. "Well, as you probably know, things came to an ugly head with McCarthy reigning in Washington, and I was one of the people temporarily suspended from school."

She broke off and we both waited, the ice in our glasses melted and the drinks gone flat.

"At first, I didn't mind," she said finally. "After all, we were right. The fact that they suspended us proved it. Besides, I was in the middle of an affair, a real one this time, and too busy with that to care about anything else." She paused again, frowning.

"He was white," she said quickly and glanced at me as though to surprise either shock or disapproval in my face. "We were very involved. At one point—I think just after we had been suspended and he started working—we even thought of getting married. Living in New York, moving in the crowd we did, we might have been able to manage it. But I couldn't. There were too many complex things going on beneath the surface," she said, her voice strained by the hopelessness she must have felt then, her hands shaping it in the air between us. "Neither one of us could really escape what our color had come to mean in this country. Let me explain. Bob was always, for some odd reason, talking about how much the Negro suffered, and although I would agree with him I would also try to get across that, you know, like all people we also had fun once in a while, loved our children, liked making love—that we were human beings, for God's sake. But he

only wanted to hear about the suffering. It was as if this comforted him and eased his own suffering—and he did suffer
because of any number of things: his own uncertainty, for
one, his difficulties with his family, for another. . . .

"Once, I remember, when his father came into New York,
Bob insisted that I meet him. I don't know why I agreed to
go with him. . . ." She took a deep breath and raised her head
very high. "I'll never forget or forgive the look on that old
man's face when he opened his hotel-room door and saw me.
The horror. I might have been the personification of every
evil in the world. His inability to believe that it was his son
standing there holding my hand. His shock. I'm sure he never
fully recovered. I know I never did. Nor can I forget Bob's
laugh in the elevator afterwards, the way he kept repeating:
'Did you see his face when he saw you? Did you. . . ?' He had
used me, you see. I had been the means, the instrument of
his revenge.

"And I wasn't any better. I used him. I took every opportunity to treat him shabbily, trying, you see, through him, to
get at that white world which had not only denied me, but
had turned my own against me." Her eyes closed. "I went
numb all over when I understood what we were doing to,
and with, each other. I stayed numb for a long time."

As Reena described the events which followed—the break
with Bob, her gradual withdrawal from the left-wing group
("I had had it with them too. I got tired of being 'their Negro,' their pet. Besides, they were just all talk, really. All
theories and abstractions. I doubt that, with all their elab-
orate plans for the Negro and for the workers of the world,
any of them had ever been near a factory or up to Harlem")—
as she spoke about her reinstatement in school, her voice suggested the numbness she had felt then. It only stirred into life
again when she talked of her graduation.

"You should have seen my parents. It was really their day.
My mother was so proud she complained about everything:
her seat, the heat, the speaker; and my father just sat there

long after everybody had left, too awed to move. God, it meant so much to them. It was as if I had made up for the generations his people had picked cotton in Georgia and my mother's family had cut cane in the West Indies. It frightened me."

I asked her after a long wait what she had done after graduating.

"How do you mean, what I did. Looked for a job. Tell me, have you ever looked for work in this man's city?"

"I know," I said, holding up my hand. "Don't tell me."

We both looked at my raised hand which sought to waive the discussion, then at each other and suddenly we laughed, a laugh so loud and violent with pain and outrage it brought tears.

"Girl," Reena said, the tears silver against her blackness. "You could put me blindfolded right now at the Times Building on 42nd Street and I would be able to find my way to every newspaper office in town. But tell me, how come white folks is so *hard?*"

"Just bo'n hard."

We were laughing again and this time I nearly slid off the trunk and Reena fell back among the satin roses.

"I didn't know there were so many ways of saying 'no' without ever once using the word," she said, the laughter lodged in her throat, but her eyes had gone hard. "Sometimes I'd find myself in the elevator, on my way out, and smiling all over myself because I thought I had gotten the job, before it would hit me that they had really said no, not yes. Some of those people in personnel had so perfected their smiles they looked almost genuine. The ones who used to get me, though, were those who tried to make the interview into an intimate chat between friends. They'd put you in a comfortable chair, offer you a cigarette, and order coffee. How I hated that coffee. They didn't know it—or maybe they did—but it was like offering me hemlock. . . .

"You think Christ had it tough?" Her laughter rushed

against the air which resisted it. "I was crucified five days a week and half-day on Saturday. I became almost paranoid. I began to think there might be something other than color wrong with me which everybody but me could see, some rare disease that had turned me into a monster.

"My parents suffered. And that bothered me most, because I felt I had failed them. My father didn't say anything but I knew because he avoided me more than usual. He was ashamed, I think, that he hadn't been able, as a man and as my father, to prevent this. My mother—well, you know her. In one breath she would try to comfort me by cursing them: 'But Gor blind them,' "—and Reena's voice captured her mother's aggressive accent—" 'if you had come looking for a job mopping down their floors they would o' hire you, the brutes. But mark my words, their time goin' come, 'cause God don't love ugly and he ain't stuck on pretty. . .' And in the next breath she would curse me, 'Journalism! Whoever heard of colored people taking up journalism. You must feel you's white or something so. The people is right to chuck you out their office. . .' Poor thing, to make up for saying all that she would wash my white gloves every night and cook cereal for me in the morning as if I were a little girl again. Once she went out and bought me a suit she couldn't afford from Lord and Taylor's. I looked like a Smith girl in blackface in it. . . . So guess where I ended up?"

"As a social investigator for the Welfare Department. Where else?"

We were helpless with laughter again.

"You too?"

"No," I said, "I taught, but that was just as bad."

"No," she said, sobering abruptly. "Nothing's as bad as working for Welfare. Do you know what they really mean by a social investigator? A spy. Someone whose dirty job it is to snoop into the corners of the lives of the poor and make their poverty more vivid by taking from them the last shred of privacy. 'Mrs. Jones, is that a new dress you're wearing?' 'Mrs.

Brown, this kerosene heater is not listed in the household
items. Did you get an authorization for it?' 'Mrs. Smith, is
that a telephone I hear ringing under the sofa?' I was utterly
demoralized within a month.

"And another thing. I thought I knew about poverty. I
mean, I remember, as a child, having to eat soup made with
those white beans the government used to give out free for
days running, sometimes, because there was nothing else. I
had lived in Brownsville, among all the poor Jews and Poles
and Irish there. But what I saw in Harlem where I had my
case load was different somehow. Perhaps because it seemed
so final. There didn't seem to be any way to escape from those
dark hallways and dingy furnished rooms . . . All that defeat." Closing her eyes, she finished the stale whiskey and
soda in her glass.

"I remember a client of mine, a girl my age with three
children already and no father for them and living in the expensive squalor of a rooming house. Her bewilderment. Her
resignation. Her anger. She could have pulled herself out of
the mess she was in? People say that, you know, including
some Negroes. But this girl didn't have a chance. She had
been trapped from the day she was born in some small town
down South.

"She became my reference. From then on and even now,
whenever I hear people and groups coming up with all kinds
of solutions to the quote Negro problem, I ask one question.
What are they really doing for that girl, to save her or to save
the children? . . . The answer isn't very encouraging."

It was some time before she continued and then she told me
that after Welfare she had gone to work for a private social-
work agency, in their publicity department, and had started
on her master's in journalism at Columbia. She also left home
around this time.

"I had to. My mother started putting the pressure on me
to get married. The hints, the remarks—and you know my

mother was never the subtle type—her anxiety, which made
me anxious about getting married after a while. Besides, it
was time for me to be on my own."

In contrast to the unmistakably radical character of her late
adolescence (her membership in the left-wing group, the affair with Bob, her suspension from college), Reena's life of
this period sounded ordinary, standard—and she admitted it
with a slightly self-deprecating, apologetic smile. It was similar to that of any number of unmarried professional Negro
women in New York or Los Angeles or Washington: the job
teaching or doing social work which brought in a fairly decent salary, the small apartment with kitchenette which they
sometimes shared with a roommate; a car, some of them;
membership in various political and social action organizations for the militant few like Reena; the vacations in Mex-
ico, Europe, the West Indies, and now Africa; the occasional
date. "The interesting men were invariably married," Reena
said and then mentioned having had one affair during that
time. She had found out he was married and had thought of
her only as the perfect mistress. "The bastard," she said, but
her smile forgave him.

"Women alone!" she cried, laughing sadly, and her raised
opened arms, the empty glass she held in one hand made eloquent their aloneness. "Alone and lonely, and indulging
themselves while they wait. The girls of the houseplan have
reached their majority only to find that all those years they
spent accumulating their degrees and finding the well-paying
jobs in the hope that this would raise their stock have, instead, put them at a disadvantage. For the few eligible men
around—those who are their intellectual and professional
peers, whom they can respect (and there are very few of
them)—don't necessarily marry them, but younger women
without the degrees and the fat jobs, who are no threat, or
they don't marry at all because they are either queer or
mother-ridden. Or they marry white women. Now, intellec-
tually I accept this. In fact, some of my best friends are white

women . . ." And again our laughter—that loud, searing burst
which we used to cauterize our hurt mounted into the unac-
cepting silence of the room. "After all, our goal is a fully integrated society. And perhaps, as some people believe, the
only solution to the race problem is miscegenation. Besides,
a man should be able to marry whomever he wishes. Emotionally, though, I am less kind and understanding, and I
resent like hell the reasons some black men give for rejecting
us for them."

"We're too middle-class-oriented," I said. "Conservative."

"Right. Even though, thank God, that doesn't apply to
me."

"Too threatening . . . castrating . . ."

"Too independent and impatient with them for not being
more ambitious . . . contemptuous . . ."

"Sexually inhibited and unimaginative . . ."

"And the old myth of the excessive sexuality of the black
woman goes out the window," Reena cried.

"Not supportive, unwilling to submerge our interests for
theirs . . ."

"Lacking in the subtle art of getting and keeping a
man . . ."

We had recited the accusations in the form and tone of a
litany, and in the silence which followed we shared a thin,
hopeless smile.

"They condemn us," Reena said softly but with anger,
"without taking history into account. We are still, most of us,
the black woman who had to be almost frighteningly strong
in order for us all to survive. For, after all, she was the one
whom they left (and I don't hold this against them; I understand) with the children to raise, who had to *make* it somehow or the other. And we are still, so many of us, living that
history.

"You would think that they would understand this, but
few do. So it's up to us. We have got to understand them and
save them for ourselves. How? By being, on one hand, persons

in our own right and, on the other, fully the woman and the wife. . . . Christ, listen to who's talking! I had my chance. And I tried. Very hard. But it wasn't enough."

The festive sounds of the wake had died to a sober murmur beyond the bedroom. The crowd had gone, leaving only Reena and myself upstairs and the last of Aunt Vi's closest friends in the basement below. They were drinking coffee. I smelled it, felt its warmth and intimacy in the empty house, heard the distant tapping of the cups against the saucers and voices muted by grief. The wake had come full circle: they were again mourning Aunt Vi.

And Reena might have been mourning with them, sitting there amid the satin roses, framed by the massive headboard. Her hands lay as if they had been broken in her lap. Her eyes were like those of someone blind or dead. I got up to go and get some coffee for her.

"You met my husband." She said quickly, stopping me.

"Have I?" I said, sitting down again.

"Yes, before we were married even. At an autograph party for you. He was free-lancing—he's a photographer—and one of the Negro magazines had sent him to cover the party."

As she went on to describe him I remembered him vaguely, not his face, but his rather large body stretching and bending with a dancer's fluidity and grace as he took the pictures. I had heard him talking to a group of people about some issue on race relations very much in the news then and had been struck by his vehemence. For the moment I had found this almost odd, since he was so fair-skinned he could have passed for white.

They had met, Reena told me now, at a benefit show for a Harlem day nursery given by one of the progressive groups she belonged to, and had married a month afterwards. From all that she said they had had a full and exciting life for a long time. Her words were so vivid that I could almost see them: she with her startling blackness and extraordinary force and he with his near-white skin and a militancy which matched hers; both of them moving among the disaffected in New York, their stand on political and social issues equally uncompromising, the line of their allegiance reaching directly to all those trapped in Harlem. And they had lived the meaning of this allegiance, so that even when they could have afforded a life among the black bourgeoisie of St. Albans or Teaneck, they had chosen to live if not in Harlem so close that there was no difference.

"I—we—were so happy I was frightened at times. Not that anything would change between us, but that someone or something in the world outside us would invade our private place and destroy us out of envy. Perhaps this is what did happen. . . ." She shrugged and even tried to smile but she could not manage it. "Something slipped in while we weren't looking and began its deadly work.

"Maybe it started when Dave took a job with a Negro magazine. I'm not sure. Anyway, in no time, he hated it: the routine, unimaginative pictures he had to take and the magazine itself, which dealt only in unrealities: the high-society world of the black bourgeoisie and the spectacular strides Negroes were making in all fields—you know the type. Yet Dave wouldn't leave. It wasn't the money, but a kind of safety which he had never experienced before which kept him there. He would talk about free-lancing again, about storming the gates of the white magazines downtown, of opening his own studio—but he never acted on any one of these things. You see, despite his talent—and he was very talented—he had a diffidence that was fatal.

"When I understood this I literally forced him to open the studio—and perhaps I should have been more subtle and indirect, but that's not my nature. Besides, I was frightened and desperate to help. Nothing happened for a time. Dave's work was too experimental to be commercial. Gradually, though, his photographs started appearing in the prestige camera magazines and money from various awards and exhibits and an occasional assignment started coming in.

"This wasn't enough somehow. Dave also wanted the big, gaudy commercial success that would dazzle and confound that white world downtown and force it to *see* him. And yet, as I said before, he couldn't bring himself to try—and this contradiction began to get to him after awhile.

"It was then, I think, that I began to fail him. I didn't know how to help, you see. I had never felt so inadequate before. And this was very strange and disturbing for someone like me. I was being submerged in his problems—and I began fighting against this.

"I started working again (I had stopped after the second baby). And I was lucky because I got back my old job. And unlucky because Dave saw it as my way of pointing up his deficiencies. I couldn't convince him otherwise: that I had to do it for my own sanity. He would accuse me of wanting to see him fail, of trapping him in all kinds of responsibilities. . . . After a time we both got caught up in this thing, an ugliness came between us, and I began to answer his anger with anger and to trade him insult for insult.

"Things fell apart very quickly after that. I couldn't bear the pain of living with him—the insults, our mutual despair, his mocking, the silence. I couldn't subject the children to it any longer. The divorce didn't take long. And thank God, because of the children, we are pleasant when we have to see each other. He's making out very well, I hear."

She said nothing more, but simply bowed her head as though waiting for me to pass judgment on her. I don't know how long we remained like this, but when Reena finally raised her head, the darkness at the window had vanished and dawn was a still, gray smoke against the pane.

"Do you know," she said, and her eyes were clear and a smile had won out over pain, "I enjoy being alone. I don't tell people this because they'll accuse me of either lying or deluding myself. But I do. Perhaps, as my mother tells me, it's only temporary. I don't think so, though. I feel I don't ever want to be involved again. It's not that I've lost interest in men. I go out occasionally, but it's never anything serious. You see, I have all that I want for now."

Her children first of all, she told me, and from her description they sounded intelligent and capable. She was a friend as well as a mother to them, it seemed. They were planning, the four of them, to spend the summer touring Canada. "I will feel that I have done well by them if I give them, if nothing more, a sense of themselves and their worth and importance as black people. Everything I do with them, for them, is to this end. I don't want them ever to be confused about this. They must have their identifications straight from the beginning. No white dolls for them!"

Then her job. She was working now as a researcher for a small progressive news magazine with the promise that once she completed her master's in journalism (she was working on the thesis now) she might get a chance to do some minor reporting. And like most people she hoped to write someday. "If I can ever stop talking away my substance," she said laughing.

And she was still active in any number of social action groups. In another week or so she would be heading a delegation of mothers down to City Hall "to give the Mayor a little hell about conditions in the schools in Harlem." She had started an organization that was carrying on an almost door-to-door campaign in her neighborhood to expose, as she put it, "the blood suckers: all those slum lords and storekeepers with their fixed scales, the finance companies that never tell you the real price of a thing, the petty salesmen that leech off the poor. . . ." In May she was taking her two older girls on a nationwide pilgrimage to Washington to urge for a more rapid implementation of the school-desegregation law.

"It's uncanny," she said and the laugh which accompanied the words was warm, soft with wonder at herself, girlish even and the air in the room which had refused her laughter before rushed to absorb this now. "Really uncanny. Here I am, practically middle-aged, with three children to raise by myself and with little or no money to do it and yet I feel, strangely enough, as though life is just beginning—that it's new and fresh with all kinds of possibilities. Maybe it's because I've been through my purgatory and I can't ever be overwhelmed again. I don't know. Anyway, you should see me on evenings after I put the children to bed. I sit alone in the living room (I've repainted it and changed all the furniture since Dave's gone, so that it would at least look different)—I sit there making plans and all of them seem possible. The most important plan right now is Africa. I've already started saving the fare."

I asked her whether she was planning to live there permanently and she said simply, "I want to live and work there. For how long, for a lifetime, I can't say. All I know is that I have to. For myself and for my children. It is important that they see black people who have truly a place and history of their own and who are building for a new and, hopefully, more sensible world. And I must see it, get close to it because I can never lose the sense of being a displaced person here in America because of my color. Oh I know I should remain and fight not only for integration (even though, frankly, I question whether I want to be integrated into America as it stands now, with its complacency and materialism, its soullessness) but to help change the country into something better, sounder—if that is still possible. But I have to go to Africa. . . .

"Poor Aunt Vi," she said after a long silence and straightened one of the roses she had crushed. "She never really got to enjoy her bed of roses what with only Thursdays and every other Sunday off. All that hard work. All her life . . . Our lives have got to make more sense, if only for her."

We got up to leave shortly afterwards. Reena was staying on to attend the burial later in the morning, but I was taking the subway to Manhattan. We parted with the usual promise to get together and exchanged telephone numbers. And Reena did phone a week or so later. I don't remember what we talked about though.

Some months later I invited her to a party I was giving before leaving the country. But she did not come.

7

"blackwoman:" and "BLACKWOMAN"

by Don L. Lee
(First published 1969)

FROM

Don't Cry, Scream

*The black woman's liberation is partially dependent on the
black male's asserting his masculinity and destroying the
image of powerlessness which America has created for him.
If the black man provides the black woman with respect and
masculine support, her quest for a viable identity will be
eased and the black male-female schism may be mended. The
following poems, typical of the new attitude of many Afro-
Americans, vividly express the need for a conciliatory re-
alignment of black male-female relationships.*

blackwoman:

> will define herself. naturally. will
> talk/walk/live/& love her images. her
> beauty will be. the only way to be is
> to be. blackman take her. u don't need
> music to move; yr/movement toward her
> is music. & she'll do more than dance.

BLACKWOMAN

blackwoman:
is an
in and out
rightsideup
action-image
of her man..   ....
in other
(blacker) words;
she's together,
if
he
bes.

8

"To All Black Women from All Black Men"

by Eldridge Cleaver
(First published 1968)

FROM

Soul on Ice

The interrelationship of the black woman's social posture and the black man's responsibility is explained in bold, vivid language in the following selection. Comment is superfluous. Eldridge Cleaver speaks eloquently for himself and his conception of the new "Black Man" in this essay.

Queen—Mother—Daughter of Africa
Sister of My Soul
Black Bride of My Passion
My Eternal Love

I greet you, my Queen, not in the obsequious whine of a cringing Slave to which you have become accustomed, neither do I greet you in the new voice, the unctuous supplications of the sleek Black Bourgeois, nor the bullying bellow of the rude Free Slave—but in my own voice do I greet you, the voice of the Black Man. And although I greet you *anew,* my greeting is not *new,* but as old as the Sun, Moon, and Stars. And rather than mark a new beginning, my greeting signifies only my Return.

I have Returned from the dead. I speak to you now from the Here and Now. I was dead for four hundred years. For four hundred years you have been a woman alone, bereft of her man, a manless woman. For four hundred years I was neither your man nor my own man. The white man stood between us, over us, around us. The white man was your man and my man. Do not pass lightly over this truth, my Queen, for even though the fact of it has burned into the marrow of our bones and diluted our blood, we must bring it to the surface of the mind, into the realm of knowing, glue our gaze upon it and stare at it as at a coiled serpent in a baby's playpen or the fresh flowers on a mother's grave. It is to be pondered and realized in the heart, for the heel of the white man's boot is our point of departure, our point of Resolve and Return—the bloodstained pivot of our future. (But I would ask you to recall, that before we could come up from slavery, we had to be pulled down from our throne.)

Across the naked abyss of negated masculinity, of four hundred years minus my Balls, we face each other today, my Queen. I feel a deep, terrifying hurt, the pain of humiliation of the vanquished warrior. The shame of the fleetfooted sprinter who stumbles at the start of the race. I feel unjustified. I can't bear to look into your eyes. Don't you know (surely you must have noticed by now: four hundred years!) that for four hundred years I have been unable to look squarely into your eyes? I tremble inside each time you look at me. I can feel ... in the ray of your eye, from a deep hiding place, a long-kept secret you harbor. That is the unadorned truth. Not that I would have felt justified, under the circumstances, in taking such liberties with you, but I want you to know that I feared to look into your eyes because I knew I would find reflected there a merciless Indictment of my impotence and a compelling challenge to redeem my conquered manhood.

My Queen, it is hard for me to tell you what is in my heart for you today—what is in the heart of all my black brothers

for you and all your black sisters—and I fear I will fail unless
you reach out to me, tune in on me with the antenna of your
love, the sacred love in ultimate degree which you were unable to give me because I, being dead, was unworthy to receive it; that perfect, radical love of black on which our Fathers thrived. Let me drink from the river of your love at its
source, let the lines of force of your love seize my soul by its
core and heal the wound of my Castrations, let my convex
exile end its haunted Odyssey in your concave essence which
receives that it may give. Flower of Africa, it is only through
the liberating power of your *re*-love that my manhood can
be redeemed. For it is in your eyes, before you, that my need
is to be justified. Only, only, only you and only you can condemn or set me free.

Be convinced, Sable Sister, that the past is no forbidden
vista upon which we dare not look, out of a phantom fear of
being, as the wife of Lot, turned into pillars of salt. Rather
the past is an omniscient mirror: we gaze and see reflected
there ourselves and each other—what we used to be, what we
are today, how we got this way, and what we are becoming.
To decline to look into the Mirror of Then, my heart, is to
refuse to view the face of Now.

*I have died the ninth death of the cat, have seen Satan face
to face and turned my back on God, have dined in the Swine's
Trough, and descended to the uttermost echelon of the Pit,
have entered the Den and seized my Balls from the teeth of
a roaring lion!*

Black Beauty, in impotent silence I listened, as if to a
symphony of sorrows, to your screams for help, anguished
pleas of terror that echo still throughout the Universe and
through the mind, a million scattered screams across the painful years that merged into a single sound of pain to haunt
and bleed the soul, a white-hot sound to char the brain and
blow the fuse of thought, a sound of fangs and teeth sharp to

eat the heart, a sound of moving fire, a sound of frozen heat, a sound of licking flames, a fiery-fiery sound, a sound of fire to burn the steel out of my Balls, a sound of Blue fire, a Bluesy sound, the sound of dying, the sound of my woman in pain, *the sound of my woman's pain,* THE SOUND OF MY WOMAN CALLING ME, ME, I HEARD HER CALL FOR HELP, I HEARD THAT MOURNFUL SOUND BUT HUNG MY HEAD AND FAILED TO HEED IT, I HEARD MY WOMAN'S CRY, I HEARD MY WOMAN'S SCREAM, I HEARD MY WOMAN BEG THE BEAST FOR MERCY, I HEARD HER BEG FOR ME, I HEARD MY WOMAN BEG THE BEAST FOR MERCY FOR ME, I HEARD MY WOMAN DIE, I HEARD THE SOUND OF HER DEATH, A SNAPPING SOUND, A BREAKING SOUND, A SOUND THAT SOUNDED FINAL, THE LAST SOUND, THE ULTIMATE SOUND, THE SOUND OF DEATH, ME, I HEARD, I HEAR IT EVERY DAY, I HEAR HER NOW . . . I HEAR YOU NOW . . . I HEAR YOU . . . I heard you then . . . your scream came like a searing bolt of lightning that blazed a white streak down my black back. In a cowardly stupor, with a palpitating heart and quivering knees, I watched the Slaver's lash of death slash through the opposing air and bite with teeth of fire into your delicate flesh, the black and tender flesh of African Motherhood, forcing the startled Life untimely from your torn and outraged womb, the sacred womb that cradled primal man, the womb that incubated Ethiopia and populated Nubia and gave forth Pharaohs unto Egypt, the womb that painted the Congo black and mothered Zulu, the womb of Mero, the womb of the Nile, of the Niger, the womb of Songhay, of Mali, of Ghana, the womb that felt the might of Chaka before he saw the Sun, the Holy Womb, the womb that knew the future form of Jomo Kenyatta, the womb of Mau Mau, the womb of the blacks, the womb that nurtured Toussaint L'Ouverture, that warmed Nat Turner, and Gabriel Prosser, and Denmark Vesey, the black womb that surrendered up in tears that nameless and endless chain of Africa's Cream, the Black Cream of the Earth, that nameless and endless black chain that sank in heavy groans into oblivion in the great abyss, the womb that received and nourished and held firm the seed and gave back Sojourner Truth, and Sister Tubman, and Rosa Parks, and Bird, and Richard Wright, and your other works of art who wore and wear such names as Marcus Garvey and Du Bois and Kwame Nkrumah and Paul Robeson and Malcolm X and Robert Williams, and the one you bore in pain and called Elijah Muhammad, but most of all that nameless one they tore out of your womb in a flood of murdered blood that splashed upon and seeped into the mud. And Patrice Lumumba, and Emmett Till, and Mack Parker.

O, My Soul! I became a sniveling craven, a funky punk, a vile, groveling bootlicker, with my will to oppose petrified by a cosmic fear of the Slavemaster. Instead of inciting the Slaves to rebellion with eloquent oratory, I soothed their hurt and eloquently sang the Blues! Instead of hurling my life with contempt into the face of my Tormentor, *I shed your precious blood!* When Nat Turner sought to free me from my Fear, my Fear delivered him up unto the Butcher—a martyred monument to my Emasculation. My spirit was unwilling and my flesh was weak. Ah, eternal ignominy!

I, the Black Eunuch, divested of my Balls, walked the earth with my mind locked in Cold Storage. I would kill a black man or woman quicker than I'd smash a fly, while for the white man I would pick a thousand pounds of cotton a day. What profit is there in the blind, frenzied efforts of the (Guilty!) Black Eunuchs (Justifiers!) who hide their wounds and scorn the truth to mitigate their culpability through the pallid sophistry of postulating a Universal Democracy of Cowards, pointing out that in history no one can hide, that if not at one time then surely at another the iron heel of the conquerer has ground into the mud the Balls of Everyman? Memories of yesterday will not assuage the torrents of blood that flow today from my crotch. Yes, History could pass for a scarlet text, its jot and tittle graven red in human blood. More armies than shown in the books have planted flags on foreign soil leaving Castration in their wake. But no Slave should die a natural death. There is a point where Caution ends and Cowardice begins. Give me a bullet through the brain from the gun of the beleaguered oppressor on the night of siege. Why is there dancing and singing in the Slave Quarters? A Slave who dies of natural causes cannot balance two dead flies in the Scales of Eternity. Such a one deserves rather to be pitied than mourned.

Black woman, without asking how, just say that we survived our forced march and travail through the Valley of Slavery, Suffering, and Death—there, that Valley there beneath us hidden by that drifting mist. Ah, what sights and sounds and pain lie beneath that mist! And we had thought that our hard climb out of that cruel valley led to some cool, green and peaceful, sunlit place—but it's all jungle here, a wild and savage wilderness that's overrun with ruins.

But put on your crown, my Queen, and we will build a New City on these ruins.

Biographies of Contributors

MAYA ANGELOU is a dancer, choreographer, actress and writer. She appeared in Jean Genêt's *The Blacks*, and *Cabaret for Freedom*, a play which, in collaboration with Godfrey Cambridge, she also produced and directed. Presently residing in New York City, she has lived in Africa where she has written for newspapers.

JAMES BALDWIN is the most widely acclaimed black writer of recent years. He was born in New York City in 1924 and, as a youth, was a preacher in Harlem's storefront churches. He won a Eugene Saxton Fellowship three years after graduating from high school and, in 1953, published his first novel, *Go Tell It on the Mountain*. Although he has published three novels, two plays and numerous short stories, his literary reputation is based primarily on his essays and he is considered a contemporary master of that form.

BOB BENNETT is a twenty-three-year-old poet who has attended Fordham University. He has stated that "I began to write in order to put some of my blackness and soul in ink for myself and my people."

BENJAMIN ALBERT BOTKIN was Folklore Editor of the Federal Writers Project in Washington, D.C., during 1938 and 1939. From 1942 to 1945 he was director of the Archive of American Folk Songs at the Library of Congress. A teacher and writer, he has published numerous books including *A Treasury of American Folklore*.

GWENDOLYN BROOKS was born in Topeka, Kansas in 1917. Her first volume of poems, *A Street in Bronzeville*, was published in 1945. Five years later she won the Pulitzer prize for a book of poetry entitled *Annie Allen*. In addition to her poetry, she has written fiction and in 1953 published a novel, *Maud Martha*.

CLAUDE BROWN was born in New York in 1937. His best-selling autobiography, published when he was twenty-eight years old, describes his early life in Harlem. Despite the success of his first book, he has professed no literary ambitions. He has attended Howard University and Rutgers University and intends to pursue a career in law and politics.

JOSEPHINE CARSON was born in Tulsa, Oklahoma, and attended Tulsa University and the University of California in Los Angeles. She is a journalist and author and has published two books prior to *Silent Voices*.

ELDRIDGE CLEAVER was born in Little Rock, Arkansas, in 1935. He was educated in ghettos in Los Angeles and in various California state prisons. He had been Minister of Information for the Black Panther party before he went into "political exile" in Algiers in 1969. Cleaver has published two other volumes of essays since *Soul on Ice* in 1968; he has also written articles for *Ramparts, Esquire, Black Dialogue, Liberator* and *Mademoiselle*.

LUCILLE CLIFTON is the mother of six children and lives in Baltimore, Maryland. *Good Times* was her first book of poetry, although her poems have appeared in various journals and magazines.

ROBERT COLES, M.D., is a research psychiatrist at the Harvard University Health Services. He is the author of the acclaimed *Children of Crisis* and a more recent psychological study of the early life of migrant farm workers, *Uprooted Children*.

MARTIN B. DUBERMAN teaches history at Princeton University. In addition to his play, *In White America,* he is the author of *James Russell Lowell* and the 1962 Bancroft prize-winning *Charles Francis Adams: 1807–1886,* both biographies.

W. E. B. Du BOIS was one of the most prominent black critics, scholars, authors and civil rights leaders of the twentieth century. Born in Great Barrington, Massachusetts, he received his B.A. from Fisk University and his Ph.D. from Harvard. In 1909 he helped found the N.A.A.C.P. and was editor of its official publication, *Crisis*. Among his books are *The Souls of Black Folk, The Philadelphia Story,* and *Dusk and Dawn.* Du Bois emigrated to Africa in 1961 and two years later died in Ghana while working on a proposed Encyclopaedia Africana.

MARI EVANS, a native of Toledo, Ohio, was educated at the University of Toledo. Her poems have been published in numerous textbooks and anthologies. She is a John Hay Whitney Fellow, and writer in residence at Indiana University. Her book *I Am A Black Woman* has been published by William Morrow.

E. FRANKLIN FRAZIER (1894–1962) was one of the most prominent black historians and sociologists of the twentieth century. Born in Baltimore, Maryland, he attended Howard University and received his Ph.D. from the University of Chicago. He taught at Howard University from 1934 to 1959, becoming the chairman of the sociology department. Among the books that he published, *Black Bourgeoisie* was the most controversial and widely acclaimed.

LETHONIA GEE was born in Harlem and spent the first eleven years of her life there. Although married now, and attending school, she still finds time to write.

WILLIAM H. GRIER, M.D., and PRICE M. COBBS, M.D., are assistant professors of psychiatry at the University of California Medical Center. They are both psychiatrists with private practices.

LORRAINE HANSBERRY (1930–1965) was born in Chicago, Illinois, and became interested in drama while still in high school. She attended Chicago's Art Institute and the University of Wisconsin. Her first play, *A Raisin in the Sun,* won the New York Drama Critics Circle Award in 1959.

FRANCES E. W. HARPER (1825–1911) was born of free parents
in Baltimore, Maryland, where she was educated before moving
to Ohio. She taught at Union Seminary in Columbia for a time,
then became involved in the reform movements (Anti-Slavery
Society, Woman's Christian Temperance Union, etc.) which,
along with her poetry, occupied most of her life. She published
four volumes of poetry during her lifetime.

CALVIN C. HERNTON is a poet and essayist who holds an M.A.
in sociology from Fisk University. Among his books are a volume
of poetry, *The Coming of Chronos to the House of Nightsong*,
and *White Papers for White Americans*, a collection of essays.

BILLIE HOLIDAY (1915–1959), perhaps better known as "Lady
Day," is a legendary figure in Afro-American music. Born in Baltimore, Maryland, she came to New York City in 1929 and began
her singing career in Harlem's cabarets. She became one of the
most famous blues singers in America and is often compared with
blues luminaries such as Ma Rainey and Bessie Smith, although
those singers apparently had little influence on her style.

LENA HORNE was born in Brooklyn, New York, in 1917. Her
stage career began in 1933, when she joined the Cotton Club's
chorus line as a dancer. She has since gained an international reputation as a singer and film star, appearing in such films as *Cabin
in the Sky* (1943), *Stormy Weather* (1943) and *Meet Me in Las
Vegas* (1956).

LANGSTON HUGHES (1902–1967) was considered "the Negro
poet laureate" of his time. Born in Joplin, Missouri, he studied
at Columbia University and Lincoln University in Pennsylvania.
Hughes's works include drama, essays and fiction, and before his
death he published more than twelve volumes of poetry. He was
one of the most prolific of America's black poets and, perhaps,
the only one who lived entirely on his professional earnings.

FENTON JOHNSON (1888–1958) was born in Chicago, Illinois,
and attended the University of Chicago. Active in Chicago literary
circles, Johnson published poems in *Poetry* magazine as early as
1918. Although he did not become a major black literary figure,

he is said to have been one of the first blacks to turn to the "new poetry" movement in America.

MALCOLM X (1925–1965) became nationally prominent in the 1950's as a spokesman for the Black Muslims, a religious sect. Until his assassination at Harlem's Audubon Ballroom, he was one of the most outspoken advocates of black militancy and the human rights struggle. Born in Omaha, Nebraska, he was educated primarily in the streets and in various reform schools and prisons. His autobiography remains one of the most illuminating and best-selling books on the American black's experience.

PAULE MARSHALL was born in Brooklyn in 1929. A graduate of Brooklyn College, she is the author of a collection of short stories, *Soul Clap Hands and Sing,* and two novels, *Brown Girl, Brownstones* and *The Chosen Place, The Timeless People.*

JEAN TOOMER (1894–1967) is the author of *Cane,* one of the best novels written by an American black. Born in Washington, D.C., and educated at the University of Wisconsin and City College of New York, Toomer was one of the leading writers of the 1920's Negro Renaissance. Although *Cane* sold only five hundred copies on publication, it has belatedly received the critical acclaim that it deserves.

RICHARD WRIGHT (1908–1960) is one of America's most important black writers. Born in Natchez, Mississippi, he grew up in the South, receiving little formal education. His first book, *Uncle Tom's Children,* was published in 1938, after he had moved to Chicago. His most famous book, *Native Son,* published in 1940, was his classic autobiography, the first novel written by a black man to become a Book-of-the-Month Club selection. It made Wright internationally famous. After the publication of *Black Boy* in 1945, Wright went to Paris, where he lived until his death.

FRANK YERBY has been the most commercially successful black writer in America for more than twenty years. Born in Augusta, Georgia, in 1916, he studied at Fisk University and the University of Chicago. He has published twenty novels and earned over 10 million dollars during his writing career.